Volume 16
SHAVER

STATICS

The ILLUSTRATED
SCIENCE *and* INVENTION
ENCYCLOPEDIA

International Edition

H. S. STUTTMAN CO., INC. *publishers* New York, N.Y. 10016

how it works

Published by H. S. STUTTMAN CO., Inc.
New York, N.Y. 10016
© Marshall Cavendish Limited 1974, 1976, 1977

SHAVER, electric

The electric shaver was first introduced to the general public in 1929. It has been developed to a high degree over the past years and two main types have evolved, namely *vibrator* and *rotary* shavers. These refer to the motion of the cutting heads.

To appreciate the problems in shaving, it is necessary to know something about the hair and skin. Each hair is deeply rooted and emerges from a crater-like hole in the skin's surface. The hair is firmly attached at the root only, and if the skin is pushed down locally, it will protrude further. The hairs grow at an angle to the skin and generally point in the same direction, forming a 'grain'. Usually, the face has several areas with differing grain directions. The flexible nature of the skin is important, since it allows the hairs to be raised by stretching the skin with the finger. It also enables the guard of a shaver to guide the hairs, without them bending over, into the cutter. There are approximately 14,000 hairs in the average man's face and they vary in thickness from 0.0047 inch (0.12 mm) to 0.0086 inch (0.22 mm). They are very tough and generally grow to a length of 0.02 inch (0.5 mm) between daily shaves.

Cutting heads

The cutting head consists of two basic parts: an outer perforated guard which is designed to trap the hairs and protect the skin, and a cutter which cuts off the hair protruding through the guard.

Since the object of shaving is to cut the hair as short as possible, the guards are very thin, the actual thickness being important since too thin a guard will allow the skin to be damaged by the cutters, causing a slight rash-like irritation. Modern shavers have guard thickness of 0.002 inch (0.05 mm) to 0.0025 inch (0.064 mm), which is thinner than a sheet of paper.

In a common type of vibrator cutting head, the guard takes the form of a thin foil with closely spaced holes of approximately 0.02 inch (0.5 mm) diameter. The cutters are a series of blades arranged at right angles to the guard. They move to and fro and in so doing cut off any hairs that protrude through the holes in the guard.

A typical rotary cutting head consists of a series of slots approximately 0.011 inch (0.28 mm) wide arranged in a circular path of 0.75 inch (19.1 mm) diameter. The cutting blades run in contact with the inside of the guard and cut off any hairs that enter the slots. Six or more blades are used and are joined together to form one complete cutter which rotates at a constant speed.

During shaving, with both types of cutting head, the skin at the base of each hair is pushed down by the guard. The hair is removed and when the skin returns to its normal position the cut hair is below the surface.

Motors

The *series wound* ELECTRIC MOTOR is the most

BRAUN ELECTRIC (U.K.) LTD

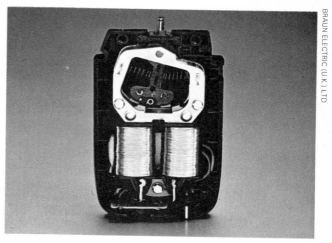

BRAUN ELECTRIC (U.K.) LTD

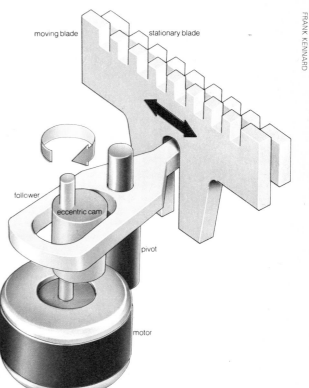

FRANK KENNARD

moving blade stationary blade

follower

eccentric cam

pivot

motor

Above right: photographs showing the cutter head (above) and motor (below) of a modern vibrator shaver. When in use, the cutter oscillates from side to side behind a perforated metal foil; it is spring loaded to ensure a good contact with the inside of the foil. The motor operates from an alternating current supply, and the two stator windings and the offset, spring loaded armature can be clearly seen in the lower picture.

Right: a diagram showing the hair trimmer mechanism of a rotary shaver. The moving blade oscillates to and fro immediately behind the stationary blade: it is operated by a pivoted cam follower which in turn is driven by an eccentrically mounted circular cam fixed to the motor shaft.

commonly used in rotary shavers. Its high starting torque and high speed of operation (about 16,000 rpm) make it particularly suitable. The motor will work on both direct current and alternating current, and different supply voltages may be accommodated by using two stator windings and a changeover switch. The cutting blades are driven through a small gearbox to reduce the cutter speed to approximately 5000 rpm and thereby increase the force available at the cutting blade. Generally, two or more cutting heads are driven by the motor.

Vibrator shaving heads are driven by a specially designed motor which has an offset, spring loaded armature pivotally mounted between the two arms of a stator winding. The end of the armature furthest from the stator is attached to the cutting block in which the blades are set, and when an alternating current supply is connected to the stator winding, the armature oscillates to and fro.

The moving parts are designed to operate at the *resonant* or natural frequency of the motor (see RESONANCE) which is twice the frequency of the supply voltage. Both the guard and the cutting block are spring loaded so that intimate contact is maintained between the blades and the inner face of the guard. There are some shavers which use a rotary motor to drive a

vibrator cutting head. In this case the to and fro motion is obtained with an eccentric CAM engaging a *follower*.

Battery shavers, often referred to as cordless shavers, usually have a motor like that of a rotary shaver but with a permanent magnet in place of the stator coils. The batteries in this type of shaver are often rechargeable.

Vibrator cutting heads will not easily trap and cut hairs longer than approximately 0.06 inch (1.5 mm), and so shavers of this type are usually fitted with a hair clipper positioned to one side of the cutting head and driven by a peg which is attached to the armature. Rotary cutting heads will cut relatively long hairs, but a clipper is often supplied for trimming moustaches and beards. These clippers are driven by means of an eccentric cam and follower.

The performance of all electric shavers depends to some extent on how they are used. Generally, vibrator shavers work at their best with fairly slow to and fro movements over the face, whereas with the rotary shaver, random motion will give good results. In both cases, a closer shave will be obtained if care is taken to stretch the skin with the finger and to shave against the grain of the beard.

Right: the cutter (above) and guard (below) of a typical rotary shaving head. The cutter has six blades and rotates at constant speed under the guard when the shaver is in use.

Below: a rotary shaver with the three shaving heads and part of the casing removed. The speed reduction gears are clearly visible in the picture.

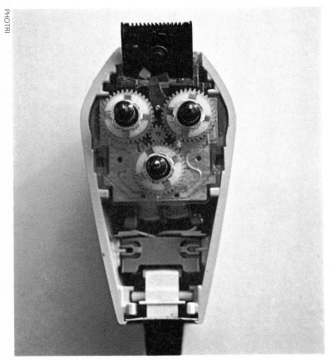

SHEET METAL FORMING

Refrigerators, office furniture, cars and many other consumer products use sheet metal in their manufacture. Most of this sheet metal is steel, but copper, brass, aluminium and other metals are also formed into various shapes by pressing them between *dies* in a *power press*.

Presses The power press is used in FORGING and DRAWING of metals, minting COINS, gramophone RECORD MANUFACTURE, and many other industrial processes. The press has tools called dies installed in it, the material to be shaped is placed in the machine between the dies, and the machine closes, forming the material.

In many cases the press is powered by HYDRAULIC MECHANISMS or by steam pressure. For example, some types of forging require a slow, steady squeeze on a piece of metal heated to a state of plasticity; hydraulic actuators provide the pressure. Other types of forging require repeated heavy hammer blows—the hammer may be lifted by means of steam pressure and dropped, the pressure being provided by the weight of the tool itself, or, in a double acting hammer, forced down by the steam pressure as well. For ordinary sheet metal forming, however, the machine is often a simple *mechanical press*.

The lower part of the press is a table called the *bolster plate* on which the lower die, or female, is installed. The upper part of the machine, which goes up and down between *guides* installed in the frame, is called the *ram*. The *punch* or *male* die is installed on the ram. In a mechanical press, the ram is connected by means of one or more *connecting rods* to a *crankshaft*, which turns in bearings installed, like the guides, in the frame of the machine, one on each side. On the side of the machine a CLUTCH, a BRAKE and a *flywheel* are connected to the end of the crankshaft. An electric motor drives the flywheel, either by means of several rubber V-belts running in grooves around its perimeter, or by means of gear teeth, in which case the flywheel is in effect a large GEAR, with teeth around its perimeter. When the operators push all the buttons, the clutch is activated, the crankshaft makes one revolution, and the ram makes one trip down toward the bolster plate and back up again. The upper die strikes the piece of metal placed on the lower die, forming it by means of the pressure or impact. The

VAUXHALL MOTORS LTD

*Above: diemakers finishing a 25-ton die set for 'drawing' floor
pans for cars. Drawing means that the metal is bent and stretched
by the dies into the necessary shape. Final grinding and polishing
are done after some test pieces have been drawn.*

pressure provided by the various types of presses varies from
less than one ton to more than 5000 tons. (Some hydraulic
forging presses have up to 50,000 tons capacity.)

Some presses have a geared flywheel on each side, and
intermediate geared shafts, pulleys or gearwheels between the
motor and the flywheel. There are also presses with eccentric
shafts instead of crankshafts; an offset section of the shaft
functions like a cam. Some presses have large gearwheels
enclosed in the top of the machine which are not flywheels but
are connected to the top of the ram by means of rods attached
to eccentric pivots.

Cutting out a shape from a piece of sheet metal upon which
other operations are then performed is called *blanking*. Punching
a hole in the metal is called *piercing* or *punching*. Certain presses
whose only function is to cut sheet metal with long horizontal
blades instead of dies are called *shears*.

Often more than one function is carried out simultaneously
during one stroke of the machine; in the forming of a car door,
for example, the door may be formed between the dies,
blanked out so that a narrow strip of scrap is separated from
the perimeter of the door, and a hole punched out for the door
handle. This is accomplished in a *double-acting* or *triple-acting*
press; the double-acting press has one ram inside the other,
and the triple-acting press has an additional ram below which
comes up instead of down. The upper, outside ram is operated
by means of a lever or *toggle* instead of by the crankshaft; such
a machine is sometimes called a *toggle press*.

Presses which make large sheet metal parts, such as for cars,
are called *straight-sided* presses and are as large as small houses.
They are constructed simply by stacking one part of the
machine on top of another, and held together by huge vertical
bolts which, at the lower end, may extend through the floor
with the nut tightened on from underneath. Installing the dies
in such machines requires large purpose-built FORK LIFT TRUCKS
and electric travelling overhead CRANES. For these reasons, the

press room in a large factory is often specially constructed.

By contrast, the *open-back inclinable* is a common type of press
for the manufacture of smaller parts. Its frame is in the shape
of a letter C and is open at the back so that the finished pieces
or the scrap may be ejected through it into storage tubs, often
by means of compressed air. It can be inclined on its base for
convenience of operation. Such a machine may be only about
eight feet (about 2.4 metres) high and four feet (1.2 m) wide.
For extremely fast production of small parts such as washers,
a *dieing press* may be used; the punch is pulled down rather than
pushed, and it may make several hundred strokes a minute,
with mechanical attachments feeding a strip of sheet metal past
the lower die.

Large presses are often automated nowadays. A common
form of automation in the production of large sheet metal
parts comprises CONVEYERS made of wide rubber belts operated
by electric motors and long steel arms with suction cups on the
ends which reach into the press and remove the blanked piece,
dropping it on the conveyer which takes it to the next operation. The reaching arms travel on a rack-and-gear device
which is operated by electrical limit switches; the suction cups
can be aided by pneumatic cylinders.

The installation of dies in presses can be a complicated
operation taking several working shifts to accomplish. Shims
(spacers) can be installed behind the dies, and the connecting
rods are made of two or more threaded parts so that they are
adjustable for length. The clearance between the dies is
carefully calculated; a mistake of a fraction of an inch in the
wrong direction will result in serious, expensive damage,
such as a broken crankshaft or damage to the dies. Springs
and pneumatic cushions are used behind dies and parts of dies
to adjust the amount of impact during operation of the press.

Safety and maintenance Safety in the press room is
of great importance. The operators of large presses must have
both hands on control buttons before the machine will
operate, to prevent careless hands from being crushed when
the ram comes down. On smaller presses, the operator may
have a tough leather strap or wire cable attached to his gloves;
the other end of the strap is connected, through tubing, to the
top of the ram, so that if the operator is careless his fingers are

jerked away from the danger area by the operation of the machine. Smaller automated presses have guards which can be raised and lowered, and must be in the down position before the machine will operate.

When the press or the dies are being repaired or adjusted, the electrical controls are 'locked out' so the machine cannot be accidentally operated, and the repairmen hold the key to the lock. In addition, large wooden beams may be placed vertically between the upper and lower dies.

Maintenance of the presses is important for safety as well as other reasons. The clutch and the brake must be properly adjusted so that the stroke of the ram begins and ends in the right position. Pound for pound, other machine tools can cost more than a press, which is a less complicated machine, but an accident with a press can be more expensive, because a damaged die or a broken crankshaft costs far more to repair or replace than a broken tool in a lathe or a milling machine. It is also interesting to note that whereas the load on a machine tool is usually continuous, the load on the bearings on a press crankshaft is concentrated at one point in its revolution, namely the point at which the ram is making contact with the lower die. For these reasons the inspection, adjustment and proper lubrication of the press is quite important, especially since a great deal of machine failure is due to improper or inadequate lubrication to begin with.

The blade on a continuously operated shear must be lubricated about once an hour by means of painting it with a soap solution. Otherwise the blade quickly becomes dull, meaning more work for the machine and jagged edges on the sheet metal being cut, increasing the chances of injury to the hands of the men handling the stock.

Diesinking Dies are made of expensive, high-quality steel blocks. A large die may be cast to the approximate pattern required before being finished; when the die cavity extends all the way through the block it may be roughed out by a FLAME CUTTING process or on a jig saw. (See also ELECTROCHEMICAL MACHINING.) Smaller die blocks can be roughed out in a *shaper* or a *band-file* (see MACHINE TOOLS).

After the block has been roughed out, most *diesinking* is done on automatic machinery. *End mill* cutters of appropriate profile are used in vertical *milling* machines, with the die block

Below left: Volkswagen roofs being finished in a Brazilian assembly plant. Metal finishers run their gloved hands over the sheet metal, finding tiny dents, ripples and 'pimples' which are almost invisible to the naked eye, but which would be glaringly evident when the piece is painted. They repair these imperfections using special tools and soft polishing wheels. The work is hot,

bolted to the table. A PANTOGRAPH may be used to follow a pattern made of plastic or sheet metal. A tracer attachment to the milling machine may follow, by means of a stylus, a model of the die made of wood or some other soft material. The surface of the die is finished to size and to a high degree of polish by means of hand scrapers, grinding wheels, polishing cloth and similar tools. *Die hobbing* is the use of a hardened and polished male plug, pushing it into a soft steel block by means of hydraulic pressure. Dies produced in this way are for limited production of simple parts, or for production in soft materials such as plastic.

Other aspects Sheet metal parts for cars, for example, are complicated to produce nowadays because designers want the finished product to have a 'sculptured' look. This often means that a single piece of metal must be bent or stretched in several directions, and that the forming must be done in several steps. The quality and composition of the metal and the

degree of forming which can take place at each step is carefully calculated; the sharper the bend in the finished piece, the less bending can be done at each step. The *clearance* between a punch and a die, or the rake on the working edges at a blanking die, is also calculated. The thinner the sheet, the less clearance is necessary. The size of the clearance affects the smoothness of the fracture when piercing metal; with less clearance the fracture will be neater but more pressure is required from the machine.

Nearly all sheet metal forming requires lubrication, so that the parts do not stick to the dies and so that the dies last longer. A wide range of soaps, oils and other materials are used, depending on the material being formed and the speed of production. Lard or sperm whale oil is used for punching copper, iron or steel. For drawing brass or copper sheet, soap dissolved in hot water is applied. Paraffin [kerosene] can be used on aluminium; aluminium can never be formed without some kind of lubrication, but on the other hand metals with a 'greasy' composition, such as tinplate, can be worked with no lubrication at all. Lubrication is applied automatically by felt rollers or manually by pads, brushes or rags. Sheet metal parts must usually be washed before they can be painted or finished.

SHIELD (see tunnelling)

dirty, noisy and requires much skill. Below centre: floor pans and other parts are clamped in jigs to be spotwelded together. When the car body has been constructed it is undercoated with primer, spray painted and then goes to the final assembly line. Below right: the press room in a car factory. The presses can be each making a different part or can be connected by conveyors.

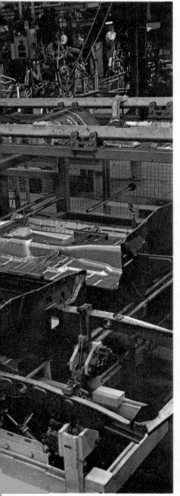

VAUXHALL MOTORS LTD

PHOTRI

SHIPS

Boats and ships of one form or another have been known for many thousands of years: certainly by 2500 BC the ancient Egyptians were building fairly sophisticated seagoing SAILING ships. Sailing ships dominated the scene from those times until the last century, when STEAM ENGINES suitable for marine use were developed. Nowadays almost all large merchant ships and WARSHIPS are built of metal and are powered by DIESEL ENGINES or steam TURBINES (see MARINE PROPULSION).

This article is concerned with modern merchant ships, and these can be divided into the following categories: *dry cargo vessels, bulk carriers, container ships, LASH* (lighter aboard ship) *vessels, passenger vessels, oil tankers* and *LPG* (liquefied petroleum gas) *vessels*.

Dry cargo vessels   The basic orthodox design for a dry cargo vessel consists of a double bottom, several holds, a midship engine room and a forward and after *peak tank*. Usually they have one or two decks and three main *superstructures*. These superstructures are a *forecastle, bridge* and a *poop* located at the bow, the middle and the stern of the ship respectively, and they extend to the sides of the vessel. The ship is subdivided with steel divisions called *bulkheads*, which are watertight from the bottom of the vessel up to the *main strength deck*. Their main function is to restrict flooding if the hull is damaged, but they also support the deck and prevent the hull from distorting owing to cargo or sea pressure.

The double bottom is a safety device in case the *bottom shell* is damaged, and it also provides a space for storage of fuel oil, water ballast or fresh water. The double bottom structure gives great strength to the bottom of the ship, which is essential for dry docking operations. The forward and after

peak tanks are normally exclusively used for water ballast to give adequate draught when the vessel is unloaded and to adjust the *trim* if necessary.

The forecastle tween decks (short for 'between') are used for bosun's stores, the storage of wire ropes and rigging equipment and for paint and lamps. On the forecastle deck, each anchor cable passes from the *windlass* (see WINCH) down through a *spurling pipe* into the *chain locker*, where the ends of the cables are connected to the fore peak bulkhead by a *cable clench*.

At the after end there is a *steering gear compartment* where a hydraulic mechanism is used to move the RUDDER. The control for the steering gear is transmitted from the wheelhouse by a *telemotor system*. Directly below the steering gear compartment is the *rudder trunk* which houses the upper *rudder stock* that is used to turn the rudder. The poop and bridge are used for accommodation and for provision stores, some of which may be refrigerated.

As diesel machinery is thermally more efficient than other types it is often used in dry cargo vessels. The propeller is driven directly from a slow speed *in line* engine. The propeller shaft passes to the after end through a *shaft tunnel*; this tunnel protects the shaft from the cargo in the holds and it provides access for maintenance of the shaft and its bearings.

In addition to the main engine, the engine room contains auxiliary machinery such as *diesel generators, oil purifiers, air compressors, ballast* and *bilge pumps, cooling water pumps* and many other essential items of equipment. Just forward of the engine room are the *settling tanks, oil fuel bunkers* and a *deep tank* port and starboard, which may be used to carry liquid cargoes or a dry cargo such as grain or sugar. The accommodation is practically all amidships with the officers berthed on the *bridge deck* or *boat deck*. The *wheelhouse*, *chartroom* and *radio room* are usually together and the captain may have his dayroom, bedroom, toilet and office on the same deck. Galleys, pantries, lavatories and recreation rooms are carefully positioned to control the noise level and prevent annoyance to the off duty crew.

The latest dry cargo vessels have the engine room nearer to the stern. This shortens the shaft length and leaves a clear deck space forward of the bridge to work the cargo. Many vessels now have deck cranes for cargo handling instead of *derricks* operated by winches, and some vessels are fitted with special heavy lifting equipment.

Bulk carriers

These are single deck, single screw vessels which carry large quantities of bulk cargo such as grain, sugar, bauxite and iron ore. The engines are installed at the after end to leave the better spaces in the hull for cargo, and the accommodation is all aft above the engine room, so that services and sanitation are concentrated in one region of the vessel. Upper and lower *wing tanks* extend over the whole length of the cargo holds and they are used for water ballast when the ship is in the unloaded or light condition to give sufficient draught to immerse the propeller and give a better control over the empty

Left: the keel of a wooden ship being constructed in Portugal.

Below: A photograph of Brunel's steamship the 'Great Eastern' taken in 1857 before the first attempt to launch her. The ship was driven by both paddles and screw, and was the largest ship afloat until she was broken up in 1889. She had a double iron hull and was designed to carry 4000 passengers, and 12,000 tons of coal for fuel.

vessel in heavy seas. The slope of the upper wing tank is designed to restrict the movement of a grain cargo, which may otherwise cause the vessel to become unstable. The double bottom tank is used for oil fuel or for water ballast, and these tanks can be used to make adjustments to the trim of the ship. Some bulk carriers have their own derricks or deck cranes, but many rely entirely on the dockside amenities for loading and discharging cargo. The hull construction for these vessels is a combination of two *framing systems* in order to obtain the best strength characteristics from each. The deck, wing tanks and double bottom are longitudinally framed and the side shell is transversely framed.

Container ships

These vessels are a relatively new concept in cargo handling which reduces the time that the vessel stays in port. The containers also form a complete load for road vehicles without further handling. British built vessels are normally designed for 20 ft (6.1 m) long containers, but they can be modified for 40 ft (12.2 m) containers if necessary. The hold length is designed to suit the length and number of containers to be fitted into the hull, and to allow sufficient space for refrigeration coolers and coupling systems for those containers with perishable cargo. The accommodation and machinery on these vessels are usually located aft to leave a clear deck for cargo working and to allow the large crane an unrestricted region for operation. The shore container crane and its *lifting spreader* system will only lift standard containers and hatch lids with correctly designed corner fittings. All the holds have vertical guides to position the containers and to give support, especially to the lowest container which could distort under the load transmitted down from those above. The containers are placed in a fore and aft attitude as the cargo

experiences less ship motion in this direction, and when lifted ashore they are more readily received by road and rail transport. One advantage of container vessels is that they can carry containers on deck, but the number of tiers depends on the strength of the hatch lids and the necessity of having a clear view from the wheelhouse. The stability of a vessel with a deck cargo must always be checked, as the centre of mass of the vessel will be raised and it may cause the ship to loll or capsize. All deck containers are lashed to the hatches with steel rods or wires having hooks and lashing screws to prevent them being lost at sea.

LASH vessels A *lighter* is a small barge which may be loaded with cargo. A LASH vessel is a mother ship which is capable of picking up loaded lighters at her stern and stowing them into large holds. The principle of the system is to collect together several loaded lighters at the same time into a rendezvous area with the LASH vessel ready for transportation over seas.

The LASH vessel has a single strength deck, forward accommodation and a semi-aft engine room. The funnel uptakes are at the sides of the vessel to allow the massive gantry crane to pass down the deck on rails. Longitudinal bulkheads, steel divisions along the length of the vessel, and transverse bulkheads, steel divisions across the vessel, form holds within the ship to stow the lighters in *cells*. Vertical barge guides are provided in the holds and the double bottom is equipped with sockets to receive the barge corner posts.

Walkways are provided with interconnecting ladders in the holds for the inspection and maintenance of the lighters. The gantry crane is supported at the stern by two large cantilevers; its lifting capacity is in excess of 500 tons and it is capable of transporting the barge along the deck to the hold. Each

lighter is handled in about 15 minutes, and at present the LASH vessel will carry about 80 lighters each with a cargo capacity of approximately 400 tons, a length of 61 ft 6 in (18.8 m) and a width of 31 ft 2 in (9.5 m). As well as being stowed in the holds, lighters can also be stowed in tiers of two on top of the large single-piece pontoon type hatch covers, which have metal fittings for keeping the lighters secure during heavy weather at sea. The crane is equipped with a hydraulically operated latching device to grip the lighters and hatch covers, and a *swell compensator* which holds the lighter steady at the stern irrespective of the relative movements of the ship and the lighter in the sea.

The advantages of the system are that cargo handling operations can be carried out in parts of the world where large ships cannot be berthed as the depth of water is insufficient. Mixed cargoes can be handled simultaneously, and the lighters can be towed to various places up river after unloading, thus providing a virtual door to door service.

Passenger vessels
In recent years the number of very large passenger liners has diminished in favour of the smaller

Left: preparing prefabricated steel sections in a Finnish shipyard.

Below left: laying the wooden deck during construction of Cunard's liner 'Queen Elizabeth 2'.

Below: a large prefabricated section about to be lifted into position during the construction of a merchant ship at Yokohama, Japan. Each section must be carefully aligned to ensure that the bottom structure of the ship remains undistorted.

vessel capable of being converted for winter cruising.

Passenger vessels are more comprehensively subdivided than other merchant ships so that if several adjacent compartments are flooded, the ship will remain stable and stay afloat. If asymmetrical flooding occurs, the vessel has cross-flooding fittings to reduce the angle of heel.

Lifeboats are fitted port and starboard on the boat deck with sufficient capacity for the total number of passengers that the ship is certified to carry. Fire control is another important safety aspect, and the vessels are subdivided vertically into *fire zones* with steel bulkheads. In these zones the bulkheads must be capable of preventing the spread of a flame in a 30 minute standard fire test, and the accommodation must have an automatic fire alarm and detection system.

A gyroscopically controlled set of STABILIZERS or *fins* are a common feature on most passenger vessels, to control the amount of roll and give a more comfortable crossing. For manœuvring, these vessels are often fitted with *bow thrusters*, and they usually have twin screw main propulsion.

The better cabins are located on the higher decks and the one, two or three berth ordinary cabins on the lower decks. One of the most important areas in the accommodation is the foyer with reception desk, purser's office, main staircase and lifts. It should be centrally placed in order to receive the passengers so that their immediate needs can be dealt with as soon as they embark. The following public rooms are quite common on most vessels: restaurants, ballroom, cinema, discotheque, shops, cocktail bars, clubrooms, banks and hairdressers. For recreation there will be a swimming pool and a deck area for games, the young children will have a nursery

SPECTRUM

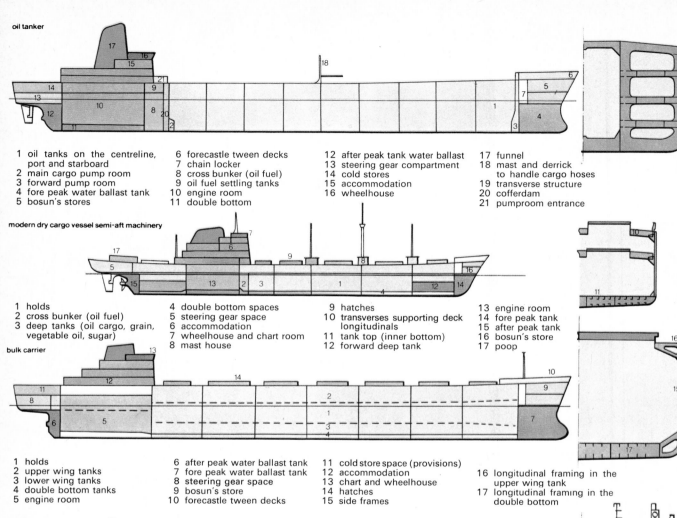

oil tanker

1 oil tanks on the centreline, port and starboard
2 main cargo pump room
3 forward pump room
4 fore peak water ballast tank
5 bosun's stores
6 forecastle tween decks
7 chain locker
8 cross bunker (oil fuel)
9 oil fuel settling tanks
10 engine room
11 double bottom
12 after peak tank water ballast
13 steering gear compartment
14 cold stores
15 accommodation
16 wheelhouse
17 funnel
18 mast and derrick to handle cargo hoses
19 transverse structure
20 cofferdam
21 pumproom entrance

modern dry cargo vessel semi-aft machinery

1 holds
2 cross bunker (oil fuel)
3 deep tanks (oil cargo, grain, vegetable oil, sugar)
4 double bottom spaces
5 steering gear space
6 accommodation
7 wheelhouse and chart room
8 mast house
9 hatches
10 transverses supporting deck longitudinals
11 tank top (inner bottom)
12 forward deep tank
13 engine room
14 fore peak tank
15 after peak tank
16 bosun's store
17 poop

bulk carrier

1 holds
2 upper wing tanks
3 lower wing tanks
4 double bottom tanks
5 engine room
6 after peak water ballast tank
7 fore peak water ballast tank
8 steering gear space
9 bosun's store
10 forecastle tween decks
11 cold store space (provisions)
12 accommodation
13 chart and wheelhouse
14 hatches
15 side frames
16 longitudinal framing in the upper wing tank
17 longitudinal framing in the double bottom

container vessel

1 container holds
2 containers on deck
3 deep tank for trimming
4 bow thruster compartment
5 fore peak tank water ballast
6 bosun's stores
7 chain locker
8 oil fuel cross bunker
9 double bottom tanks
10 engine room
11 steering gear space
12 accommodation
13 wheelhouse
14 wing tanks for water ballast
15 longitudinal girder
16 pipe and cable passage
17 after peak tank water ballast
18 duct keel

LASH vessel (lighters aboard ship)

1 holds to contain lighters
2 steering gear space
3 engine room
4 double bottom tanks
5 deep tanks
6 fore peak tanks
7 bosun's stores
8 cantilever over stern for crane support
9 accommodation
10 wheelhouse
11 lighters on deck
12 crane to lift lighters
13 lighter at stern ready to be lifted aboard
14 wing tanks
15 passage way below deck
16 funnel port and starboard

OSBORNE/MARKS

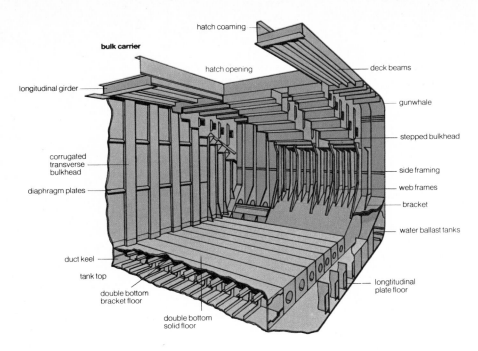

bulk carrier

hatch coaming

hatch opening

deck beams

longitudinal girder

gunwhale

stepped bulkhead

corrugated
transverse
bulkhead

side framing

web frames

diaphragm plates

bracket

water ballast tanks

duct keel

tank top

longtitudinal
plate floor

double bottom
bracket floor

double bottom
solid floor

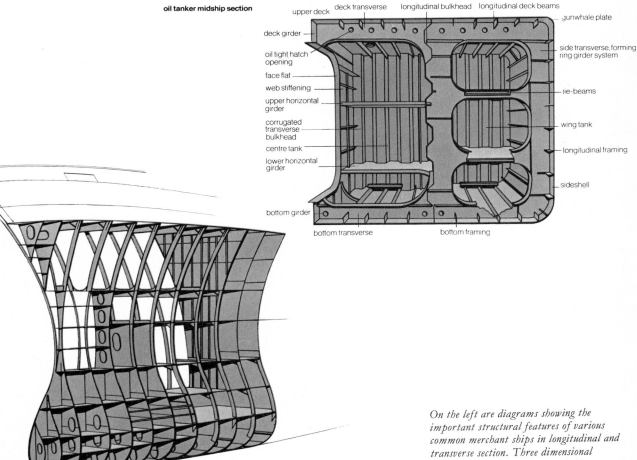

oil tanker midship section

upper deck   deck transverse   longitudinal bulkhead   longitudinal deck beams

deck girder

gunwhale plate

oil tight hatch
opening

side transverse, forming
ring girder system

face flat

web stiffening

tie-beams

upper horizontal
girder

corrugated
transverse
bulkhead

wing tank

centre tank

longitudinal framing

lower horizontal
girder

sideshell

bottom girder

bottom transverse

bottom framing

fore end construction for dry cargo ship with bulbous bow

*On the left are diagrams showing the
important structural features of various
common merchant ships in longitudinal and
transverse section. Three dimensional
representations of three selected ship
structures are shown here.*

and there are playrooms for older children. The officers are berthed near to the bridge and the remaining crew and stewards have accommodation on a lower deck.

The vessel will normally comply with the regulations of all maritime countries, including those of the US coastguard. This will then allow the vessel to change to cruising at any time.

Oil tankers

These vessels have a single main deck and a double bottom in the engine room only. Since tankers are divided into separate compartments, they are considered to be safe enough without having a double bottom along the full length of the ship. To reduce the risk of an explosion, the engines are fitted aft so that the shaft tunnel does not have to pass through any of the oil cargo tanks. At the extreme ends of the cargo tank range there is a *cofferdam* or *bunker space* to isolate the cargo from the other parts of the ship. Cofferdams are dry spaces across the vessel, preventing the possibility of any oil leaking directly into an adjacent compartment.

Pumps for discharging the cargo are fitted in a pump room in the bottom of the vessel. This pump room is often part of the cofferdam. The cargo pumps are usually driven by extended spindles from machinery in the main engine room. The oil is discharged from a tank by drawing it into the *suctions* at the end of a pipe leading from the main cargo pumps. It is then pumped vertically up from the pump room to the main deck where it passes along the deck pipelines until it reaches the deck *crossover pipes*. These crossovers are connected to the shore installations by hoses which are handled by the shore derrick. Oil tankers have small oiltight hatches with hinged lids giving access to the tanks by long steel ladders which reach to the bottom of the ship. The hatch coaming has a pipe leading vertically upwards to vent off vapour to the atmosphere if there should be a buildup of gas in the tank.

The oil tanks are subdivided by two longitudinal bulkheads into a *centre tank* and *wing tanks*, port and starboard. Sub-division of the oil tanks controls the movement of the cargo and prevents a large *free surface* across the ship which would cause it to become unstable. Tank length is also important as oil in a partially filled tank will generate a wave caused by the movement of the ship. This wave will pass up and down the tank and could cause structural damage unless it is controlled by *wash bulkheads* or restricted by the length of the tank.

The engine power of a supertanker is very large, and a single PROPELLER requires six blades so that the thrust is transmitted without overstressing the metal in any part of the blading. A *bulbous bow* is usually a standard part of the hull for a large tanker and it has the effect of modifying the flow of water at the bow, thereby reducing the power requirements from the ship's engines.

LPG vessels

Vessels of this type are designed to carry propane, butane, anhydrous ammonia and other liquefied gases in specially designed tanks, which may be rectangular or hemispherical. A typical gas tanker has a design similar to a bulk carrier but it has gas tanks built into the hull which rest on chocks and are keyed to prevent movement when the vessel is rolling or pitching. The liquid gas temperature in the

Near right: a view of the 'Queen Elizabeth 2' under construction at Clydebank, Scotland in 1966.

Far right: a supertanker under construction in a Japanese shipyard. The ship was built in a dry dock which was simply flooded when the time came to launch the ship (above right). The tanker has a capacity of 276,000 tons deadweight.

tanks may be well below zero; this will cause severe thermal stressing when the liquid moves and therefore the tanks will alter in shape owing to temperature changes. A void space between the gas tanks and the hull is filled with an INERT GAS to prevent the oxygen in the air and any leak of gas from the tank producing an explosive mixture. An inert gas unit in the engine-room is used to produce sufficient gas for the void space and to keep it topped up in case of leakage. The tanks are made from a low temperature carbon steel which must withstand impact at low temperatures and thus not be susceptible to *brittle fracture*. In some vessels the gas tanks are not refrigerated but are insulated with four inches (10.1 cm) of polyurethane foam. When the liquid gas vaporizes it collects in domes at the top of the tank where it is drawn off and passed through a *reliquefaction plant* and then returned to the tank via *condensers* in liquid form. The domes at the top of each tank project three feet (0.91 m) through the main deck.

Alternatively there may be no tank refrigeration or reliquefaction plant on the ship and the gas is free to 'boil-off'. The vapour is then transferred to the engine-room and used as bunkers for the main propulsion. This system makes the vessel less complex, cheaper on plant installation and bunkers but a percentage of the cargo is used over the voyage. Liquid gas cargo is pumped from the bottom of the tanks using submerged pumps controlled from a room amidships. During pumping a back pressure must always be maintained to prevent the gas boiling in the pump impeller and creating vapour in the *riser* when the tank is nearly emptied.

Air in the tanks is displaced before loading the liquid petroleum gas by using the inert gas system. Once the tanks are loaded they will always contain gas, so that the inerting procedure is not employed every time. Gas freeing of a cargo tank can be done by introducing inert gas until the petroleum gas is diluted below the flammable limit and then blowing air into the tank and venting the gases at the top of the mast.

Prefabricated construction   The way in which the vessel is constructed depends upon the type of ship and the technique adopted at the shipyard, and this will be influenced by the available yard machinery and cranes.

For example a bulk carrier will usually be constructed in the following way by most shipyards. Firstly the *bottom shell* and *longitudinals* will be laid on the building berth as a single unit after manufacture in the assembly shed, then the double bottom unit will be lowered on to the bottom shell and welded into position. The wing tank unit is lifted into position, aligned and welded up, and a pair of bulkheads are erected the correct distance apart over the hold length, with an allowance made for their inclination to suit the *declivity* (downslope) of the building berth (necessary for launching). A side *shell panel* can then be connected to the lower wing tank unit and bulkheads, to form the sides of the hold. Then the upper wing tank is lowered into place and welded with the remaining deck panel finally completing the amidship structure. The ship is also built forward and aft of midships simultaneously. This technique, although not adopted by every shipyard, does allow an even spread of labour force. Working from midships gives a good reference structure for taking dimensions during the building of the vessel. When each heavy unit is lifted on to the berth, the bottom of the vessel is checked for alignment by an optical system; otherwise distortion will occur.

SHOCKLEY, WILLIAM (see transistor)

SHOE MAKING (see footwear)

SHOTGUN

The earliest hand-held guns were all made for military purposes, but it was not long before they were being made for sporting use also. It was soon popular among the rich and influential to own a gun for shooting game, and there are many remaining examples which were made in the second half of the 15th century. Sporting gunmakers soon found that their patrons wanted guns which were ornamental as well as useful, and much money was invested in special presentation guns. It was not until the 18th century that sporting guns became cheap enough for the ordinary man to own, and from then on progress in design and construction was swift.

Although early guns would fire both single bullets and multiple shot, the shot firing type gradually evolved as a distinct pattern. Today shotguns are utterly different from rifles and their manufacture is a different skill altogether.

A shotgun is a smooth-bore weapon which fires a charge of small shot or pellets. It is primarily used for shooting flying birds or small ground game such as rabbits. A flying bird is almost impossible to hit with a rifle, but the shotgun launches a large number of pellets which spread out to form a distinct pattern in the air and this pattern allows the shooter to be less exact in his aim than if he were firing a rifle. The effective range is usually quite short, not much more than 30 metres or yards, and the pellets fall to the ground in a couple of hundred metres. The danger area is therefore quite small.

Most shotguns fire about one ounce (28 g), or slightly more, of lead pellets. These pellets are graded in size by a numbering system which is more than two hundred years old. The smallest size has the highest number, which in practical terms is 8 or 9. The largest has the lowest number, and this is about 3. For most game shooting size 5 or 6 is preferred. With number 6 shot there are 280 pellets to the ounce (10 per gramme).

The usual criterion of the quality of a gun is the number of pellets that it can fire into a circle 30 inches (76 cm) in diameter at a set range, usually 30 metres. A good gun, firing $1\frac{1}{8}$ ounces (31.9 g) of number 6 shot, should put 240 pellets into the circle. This allows for one pellet every 3 square inches, and means that anything inside that circle is certain to get at least one, if not more, pellets. One pellet is sufficient to kill most birds and small animals.

Clay pigeon [trap] shooters fire at thin baked-clay discs, shot into the air by a spring device, which break into fragments on being hit. They are difficult to hit and the shooter usually uses number 8 shot so as to increase the density of his pattern.

The *bore* of a shotgun is described by a number which is the number of spherical lead balls of a size to fit the bore that will add up to 1 lb (454 g) in weight. Thus, the diameter of a bore which would accept a ball 1/16th of a pound in weight, namely

1 ounce, is a 16 bore: 12 balls to the pound, a 12 bore, and so on. The method is very old and universally used. The popular 12 bore is actually 0.729 inch (1.852 cm) in diameter.

Shotgun barrels are usually tapered internally. A parallel sided barrel is called a 'cylinder'. One with a taper is said to have a 'choke'. Choking a barrel makes the shot fly in a closer pattern and so improves the chance of hitting at longer ranges when the shot from a 'cylinder' barrel would have spread so widely as to pass around the target. Choking does not increase the velocity. Shotguns rarely have the same degree of choke in both barrels. The right hand one, which is always fired first, has less choke because the target is near; the left barrel is fired second and has more choke to carry further.

The earliest shotguns were single-barreled, but sportsmen were soon asking for a second quick shot. This brought about the double-barreled gun, with the barrels side-by-side for the convenience of the primitive flintlock FIRING MECHANISMS then used. The side-by-side gun is still strongly favoured, but there are now other patterns. Clay pigeon shooters frequently use over and under barrels, a few people still prefer a single barrel; there are self-loading guns and semi-automatic loaders.

Semi-automatic guns have a magazine and are re-loaded and re-cocked by the shooter moving some part of the gun with his

A 12 bore over and under double barrel shotgun for trap shooting. A ventilated rib above the barrel dissipates heat sideways to avoid air turbulence, giving a better sight along the two small beads.

hand. Usually it is the front hand guard which is pumped to and fro, giving rise to the nickname of 'pump' guns or 'trombone' guns. Self-loading guns use the same principles as a self-loading rifle and employ recoil or gas-action to operate the mechanism. Shotgun magazines can hold up to 5 cartridges.

Shotgun cartridges (see AMMUNITION) are all parallel sided cylinders, made of cardboard or plastic, with a thin brass base. They generate low pressure, by rifle standards, and the usual muzzle velocity for the shot is just above the speed of sound. This means that the barrels can be made quite lightly, and a good double-barreled gun weighs less than 6 pounds.

Shotguns are loaded by pivoting the barrel forward and downwards, known as 'breaking'. This action ejects the spent cartridge and allows rapid re-loading.

Shotguns are made in many countries, but it is generally accepted that the finest are made in England. A gun from a top English gunmaker can cost several thousand pounds and will be fitted to the buyer as carefully as a tailor-made suit of clothes. This is done to ensure that the barrels are exactly in front of the shooter's eyes when he brings the gun to his shoulder, so that he does not have to pause to take a sight. Shotguns are aimed by instinct, and there are no sights, except on some trap-shooting guns.

Left: loading a cartridge into a 12 bore double barrel over and under shotgun. The number 5 on the cartridge refers to the pellet size, 5 or 6 being preferred for game shooting—the smaller the number the larger the size of the lead pellets.

Below: shotguns have a unique loading method, known as 'breaking', in which the barrel is pivoted forward and downward. This action also serves to eject the spent cartridges.

SHUTTER

A camera shutter controls the time during which light is allowed to fall on the film. In the early days of photography it was only necessary to take the cap off the lens, count the seconds and replace the cap. Sometimes metal flaps were mounted on the lens. These were like the shutters used on windows, which explains the origin of the word. Dry plates appeared in 1880, roll film in 1884, and the first Kodak in 1888; their increasing speed called for mechanisms to give precise exposures of fractions of a second.

Early designs   Many ingenious devices were made. The simplest was a guillotine or drop shutter, which consisted of a rectangular plate which passed in front of the lens. This could drop freely, by its own weight, or be moved by an elastic band. Variations of this system used two metal plates moving in opposite directions, or discs which rotated instead of moving in a straight line.

A completely different approach is to have the shutter not near the lens but as close as possible to the film, in the plane on which the lens focuses. These are called focal plane shutters and generally consist of a roller blind with a slit which moves across the film. Different exposures can be obtained by altering the width of the slit or the speed at which it moves. The first focal plane shutter with a variable slit was invented by William England in 1861 but it did not become popular until used in the famous Goerz Anschutz camera in 1888.

Interlens shutters   If a shutter is placed just behind or in front of a lens it will be very slightly in focus, and the image will not be evenly illuminated. When the shutter is positioned between the lens components (most lenses have more than one 'element'), the shutter will be completely defocused. Such a design is called an interlens shutter and is very popular with cameras where the lens does not need to be changed for a different one. The most simple interlens shutter has a single moving disc which is driven by a spring so that an oval hole passes in front of the lens to admit light. Often there is a second or capping plate which covers the lens while the hole is moved

Below: an interesting shutter on a Thornton Pickard camera of the 1900s, with lens removed. Pulling the cord tensions the roller blind which can then be released to give speeds as fast as 1/80 second.

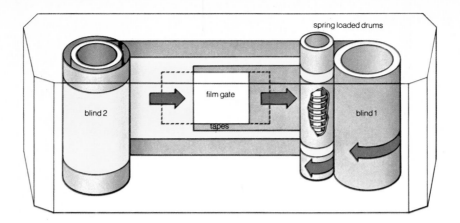

spring loaded drums

blind 2

film gate

tapes

blind 1

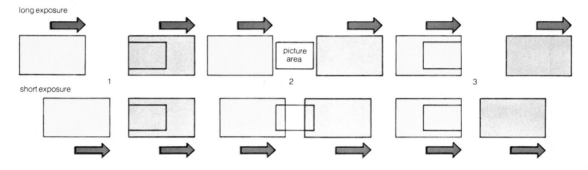

long exposure

picture area

short exposure

1   2   3

back to its original position ready for the shutter to be fired again. The spring is usually put under tension by pushing the shutter release button or lever, and since no separate setting lever is needed, the design is called *everset*.

This type of shutter is very widely used on simple cameras, and the basic design has hardly changed from the first models used on early box cameras, though the 'instantaneous' speed or I has altered from about 1/25 sec to around 1/95 sec. Other settings often given on shutters are B and T. B stands for bulb, being originally actuated by a rubber bulb and tube, and means that the shutter opens when the firing lever is pressed and stays open until released. T is for time and indicates that the shutter opens when the lever is pressed and stays open until the lever is pressed a second time. Many shutters were made in Germany and have Z for *Zeit* instead of T.

A very early complicated interlens shutter, with settings for several speeds and a separate lever to tension the spring, was the *Compound* introduced by the German firm Leckel in

Above: the mechanism of the blinds of a focal plane shutter. The blinds are always moved across at the same speed, taking something like 1/50 second to cover the whole frame. The separation between them, however, varies: the exposure given in the upper sequence would be about 1/30 second, that in the lower about 1/250 second.

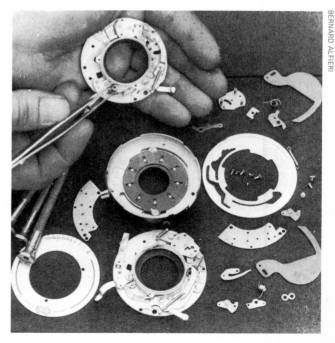

Left: the Compur type shutter of a Rolleiflex twin lens reflex camera. Shown half open, another set of blades move over to terminate the exposure. The front lens has been removed.

Right: assembling a fairly simple shutter. Curved slots in the large flat disc limit the action of projecting pins, thus controlling the shutter speed.

1902. This evolved into the famous *Compur* in 1912.

Focal plane shutters Most modern focal plane (fp) shutters have two blinds which follow each other at precise intervals. Black silk sprayed with plastic is a popular material. Usually the blinds move along the long side of the negative, which is commonly 24×36 mm (1×1½ inches). The *Contax* shutter was an exception, having metal blinds which move across the short side. A modern design, also with vertically moving metal blades, is the Japanese *Copal Square*.

Shutter speeds Normally speeds range from 1 to 1/500 second for interlens shutters and 1 to 1/1000 sec for focal plane types. Old designs have the series 1/25, 1/50, 1/100 sec and so on but the modern system runs 1/30, 1/60, 1/125 sec. Some fp types have faster speeds such as 1/2000 sec, and in the past there were exceptional models, such as the Exakta with gear trains to give speeds as long as 12 sec.

Electronic shutters Strictly speaking these are spring-operated shutters with electronic timing. Electricity stored in a capacitor discharges through an electromagnet which stops the shutter closing. Exposure time thus depends on the amount of charge in the capacitor. This allows integration of shutter and exposure metering systems for automatic exposure control. Instead of the camera's built-in EXPOSURE METER indicating a shutter speed to be set on the dial, the electrical energy from the meter cell (usually a CdS or silicon type) is used to control the capacitor charge, and hence exposure. The speeds can vary continuously instead of having to be changed in steps. Since many photographers like to know what exposure speeds are being used, there can also be associated circuitry to indicate the value. Another refinement is the provision of manually set speeds when automatic operation is not desired, and here a network of resistors does the task normally performed by delay gear wheel trains and variable spring tension. Many automatic electronic shutters can give exposures up to 20 sec.

Synchronization All shutters, even the simple ones, now have provision for being used with FLASHGUNS or bulbs. The cheapest can be used with flash bulbs or cubes at 1/30 sec. Interlens shutters can be synchronized for electronic flash (X setting) at any speed but with fp shutters the speed of the shutter must be less than about 1/60 sec, otherwise the blinds are not far enough apart to expose the whole frame area. M synchronization is for ordinary small bulbs or cubes, contact being made about 16 milliseconds before the shutter opens fully, so the bulb is burning brightly. Focal plane shutters often have an F synchronization for use with bulbs having a long burning time, which allows fast shutter speeds.

Unusual shutters One off-beat type, produced about 1945, had a gravity-assisted shutter, so the speed was about 1/100 sec when the camera was used one way up and 1/25 sec inverted, presumably with intermediate speeds when tilted sideways.

For HIGH SPEED PHOTOGRAPHY, shutters are used with blades having a continuous rotary action instead of intermittent operation. Again, movie cameras for ultra-fast recording can have rotating glass prisms or cubes to interrupt the light beam and provide successive fast exposures.

Pneumatic shutters, operated by air pressure, have also been used, notably on STEREOSCOPIC cameras, where it is an advantage to be able to supply exactly the same pressure to each of the two shutters.

SIGHT, GUN (see gunnery techniques)
SILENCER, CAR (see exhaust systems)

SILENCER (gun)

The loud noise heard when a gun is fired is due to the rapid escape of the gases from the muzzle which are produced by the explosion of the powder behind the bullet. The firearm can be effectively silenced if the escape of the gases is slowed down.

In 1908 the American Hiram Percy Maxim (1869–1936) invented a silencer for firearms. (He was the son of Sir Hiram Stevens MAXIM, who invented a MACHINE GUN, and the nephew of Hudson Maxim, who invented smokeless powders which were widely used in World War 1.) The Maxim silencer was a cylinder attached to the muzzle of the gun, comprising a series of chambers, separated from each other by metal baffles with holes in them. The bullet passed through the holes in the baffles, but the escaping gases behind the bullet expanded into the chambers, their velocity being thereby reduced so that they did not rush into the atmosphere with the force of an explosion.

The United States Army tried the Maxim silencer on rifles to be used by snipers, but it was discovered that the velocity of the bullet, which was greater than the speed of sound, caused a report of its own, so that the silencing was not effective for sniping purposes. The silencer is effective only with low velocity ammunition which travels at slightly less than the speed of sound. (The silencer is not effective on revolvers because it does not prevent the escape of gases from

Below: the silencer is screwed on to the end of the gun barrel. As the bullet speeds through the silencer, the exploding gases behind it expand into the baffles; this slows their velocity, eliminating the loud report. It also lowers the velocity of the bullet, but if the muzzle velocity of the weapon is not lowered to below the speed of sound, silencing is not completely effective.

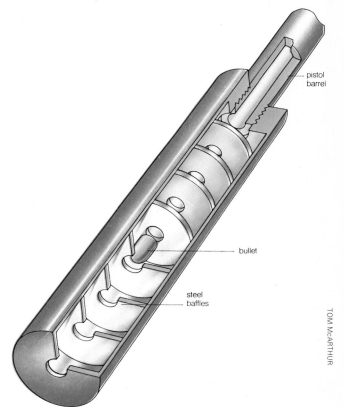

pistol barrel

bullet

steel baffles

TOM McARTHUR

COLONEL WEEKS

Above: a British Sterling sub-machine gun, when fitted with a silencer, has holes drilled in the barrel and the automatic firing provision removed. Standard ammunition is used; the expanding gases behind the bullet escape through the holes into the baffles of the silencer, lowering the velocity of the bullet to below the speed of sound. Automatic firing causes such vibration that the second bullet out of the muzzle would tear off the end of the silencer. The 1908 German Luger automatic pistol (below) uses low-velocity ammunition with its silencer.

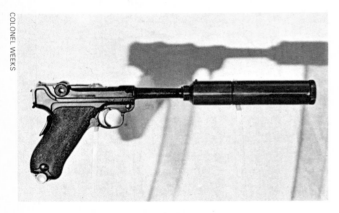

COLONEL WEEKS

around the revolving, chambered cylinder which holds the cartridges.)

During World War 2 the silencer was used by both the German and Soviet armies with low velocity ammunition. The ammunition was standard military issue except for a smaller powder charge. Silencers have usually been similar to Maxim's original; one exception, used during the war, was a simple tube with vent holes drilled in it and closed on the end with rubber discs. The bullet passed through the rubber discs, which had to be frequently replaced, while the gases escaped more slowly through the vent holes.

In 1932, as a result of bank-robbing and general lawlessness caused by the Great Depression and the Prohibition Amendment of 1917, the National Firearms Act was passed in the United States. Sawn off shotguns, for example, which are easy to conceal and have tremendous power at short range, were outlawed, and silencers were to be registered and taxed. This restricted the circulation of silencers, but the criminal elements were not notorious for obeying the law.

SILICON

The ELEMENT silicon (symbol Si) accounts for about 25% of the Earth's crust; it is second only to oxygen in abundance. Its name is derived from the Latin *silex*, which means 'flint'. The *silicates*, compounds containing silicon and oxygen, are the main components of more than 95% of the rocks found on Earth.

Although very common, silicon does not occur naturally in the pure form, and it was not until relatively late that the element was finally isolated. An early stumbling-block was the well known inertness of the compound *silica*, SiO_2, which occurs naturally as quartz or sand. The first investigators thought that silica was itself an element and did not therefore make any attempt to determine its atomic composition. In 1787 LAVOISIER suggested that silica might be the oxide of an undiscovered element, but it was not until 1823 that BERZELIUS confirmed this hypothesis by preparing an impure sample of elemental silicon for the first time. Pure, crystalline silicon was first prepared in 1854 by a method developed by the French chemist H Sainte-Claire Deville.

Pure silicon is a dull grey solid with a diamond crystal lattice. It melts at 1420°C (2588°F) and, although it is a non-metallic element, it has a distinct metallic lustre.

Production On a commercial scale silicon is prepared by reducing silica (see OXIDATION AND REDUCTION) with carbon in an electric furnace:

$$SiO_2 + 2C \longrightarrow Si + 2CO$$

silica   carbon   silicon   carbon monoxide

The resulting silicon is about 98% pure and, while this is suitable for many purposes, it is not sufficiently pure for making SEMICONDUCTORS, which nowadays is one of the most important uses of silicon. For this application the silicon is converted into TRICHLOROSILANE, $SiHCl_3$, a volatile compound which can easily be purified by DISTILLATION. The purified trichlorosilane is then decomposed on to a silicon rod in the presence of hydrogen at a temperature of about 1200°C (2192°F):

$$SiHCl_3 + H_2 \longrightarrow Si + 3HCl$$

trichlorosilane   hydrogen   silicon   hydrogen chloride

The silicon produced by this method is extremely pure: it contains less than one part per million of impurities and is ideal for making semiconductor devices such as TRANSISTORS, RECTIFIERS and solar batteries. The less pure grade of silicon is a suitable starting material for the production of *silicone polymers* (see below) and it is used as an alloying element for strengthening such metals as aluminium, copper and magnesium.

The most common silicon compound is silica, and this finds applications in the CERAMICS industry, in the manufacture of GLASS, as a refractory lining for metallurgical FURNACES, and (in the form of quartz) in PIEZOELECTRIC crystals and crystals for controlling the frequency of radio OSCILLATORS. If silica is reduced with excess carbon in an electric furnace, silicon carbide, SiC, is formed. This is a black crystalline compound which is widely used as an abrasive material because of its extreme hardness; it is commonly known as 'Carborundum' or 'Crystolon'.

Silicate minerals are widely distributed in the Earth's crust, and many of them are of commercial importance. Clay, for example, is a hydrated (water-containing) aluminium silicate, ASBESTOS is a calcium magnesium silicate and *mica*, used in the

M M RATHORE

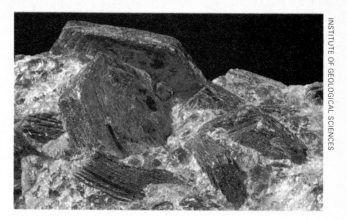

INSTITUTE OF GEOLOGICAL SCIENCES

Left: a single crystal rod of silicon which will be used to make semiconductor devices.

Right: muscovite, a type of mica, is a silicon-containing mineral. Mica is widely used in the electrical industry as an insulating material.

Below: a fabric impregnated with a silicone polymer becomes water repellant. Silicones are also used where high temperature resistance is important.

manufacture of CAPACITORS and other electrical components, is the name given to a group of silicate minerals containing potassium, aluminium and sometimes magnesium. Although some silicates can be written as a chemical formula—for example, *muscovite* (a type of mica) is $H_2KAl_3(SiO_4)_3$—many have extremely complex structures and cannot be accurately represented in this way.

Silicon tetrachloride, $SiCl_4$, which can be made by direct combination of the elements, produces a dense white smoke when exposed to moist air, and, in combination with ammonia, NH_3, it has formed the basis of a military smoke screen composition:

$$SiCl_4 + 4NH_3 + 2H_2O \rightarrow SiO_2 + 4NH_4Cl$$

silicon tetrachloride / ammonia / water vapour / silica / ammonium chloride

The smoke consists of tiny particles of silica and ammonium chloride, which are both white crystalline solids.

Silicones

The silicone POLYMERS form one of the most important groups of compounds to be developed in recent years. These polymers are similar to organic polymers except that instead of being based on chains of carbon atoms, they have chains of alternating silicon and oxygen atoms. Two organic groups, often *methyl* groups (—CH_3), are attached to each silicon atom, so a silicone polymer molecule can be written as:

$$-\underset{R'}{\overset{R}{Si}}-O-\underset{R'}{\overset{R}{Si}}-O-\underset{R'}{\overset{R}{Si}}-O-$$

where R and R′ represent the organic groups. These polymers may be liquids, plastics or rubbers, and they have good lubricating properties, good resistance to oxidation and stability at high temperatures. Greases for use at very high or very low

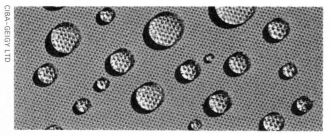

CIBA-GEIGY LTD

temperatures are often based on silicone polymers, and so are some plastic coatings designed to withstand temperatures in the range 300 to 500°C (572 to 932°F). Silicones are usually excellent electrical insulators and so they are ideal for encapsulating electronic components.

One of the most common silicones is *polydimethyl siloxane*, which has the formula already given with both R and R′ representing methyl groups. It is prepared by first reacting silicon with methyl chloride, CH_3Cl, in the presence of a catalyst containing copper and copper oxide to produce a mixture of compounds, the most important being *dichlorodimethyl silane*, $(CH_3)_2SiCl_2$:

$$2CH_3Cl + Si \longrightarrow (CH_3)_2SiCl_2$$

methyl chloride / silicon / dichlorodimethyl silane

This compound is separated from the other products by distillation and then polymerized by a carefully controlled *hydrolysis* reaction:

$$n(CH_3)_2SiCl_2 + nH_2O \rightarrow \left[-\underset{CH_3}{\overset{CH_3}{Si}}-O- \right]_n + 2nHCl$$

dichlorodimethyl silane / water / polydimethyl siloxane / hydrogen chloride

The letter 'n' simply denotes a large number whose exact value will depend on the conditions under which the reaction is carried out. *Silicone rubber* consists of a polymer of this type mixed with powdered silica and a peroxide curing agent. The peroxide acts as a crosslinking agent, like sulphur in the vulcanization of RUBBER, to produce linkages consisting either of oxygen atoms or dimethylene groups (—CH_2CH_2—) between silicon atoms in adjacent polymer chains.

A silicone rubber is ideal for making surgical implants such as artificial heart valves, because it is one of the few materials which is well tolerated by the human body. Silicone rubbers also form the basis of a number of adhesives and sealing compositions which can be used in applications where conventional compositions would be ineffective. Such adhesives can form very strong, watertight bonds to glass and they are used to make such things as frameless aquaria. The 'bouncing putty' sold in some toy shops is a silicone rubber in which some boron, B, atoms are present in the silicon-oxygen polymer chain.

SILK (see fibre, natural)

SILVER

Silver is the whitest of all metals. This property, combined with its especially high reflectivity, was responsible for its Latin name *argentum*, which means white and shining. The chemical symbol for silver, Ag, is an abbreviation of the Latin.

Because it does not readily oxidize, silver can be found in the native state, that is to say in metallic form rather than as a compound, and can therefore be assumed to be one of the first metals discovered and used by man. It has been found in tombs dating from 4000 BC.

Occurrence and extraction

Today the amounts of silver collected in the native state are not commercially significant. The majority of the metal is obtained as a by-product of the extraction and purification of COPPER, NICKEL and LEAD, although ores containing the mineral *argentite* (silver sulphide, Ag_2S) are still mined in their own right.

The first important step in the development of methods of extracting silver from its ores was made soon after the opening up of the Mexican silver mines by the Spaniards early in the 16th century. It was known as the *patio process* (because it was carried out in a paved yard) and consisted of mixing the powdered ore, common salt (NaCl) and roasted copper sulphide (CuS) with water, and spreading the resulting mud over the yard. The salt and copper oxide produced copper chlorides which reacted with the silver sulphide to form silver chloride (AgCl). The silver chloride was then reduced to the metal by adding MERCURY which also served to 'mop up' the silver as an *amalgam* (solution of metal in mercury). The process was not particularly efficient and the mercury losses were alarmingly high—in fact it was said that one needed a mercury mine to run a silver mine. The patio process persisted in some areas right up to the start of this century, although it had been generally superseded by more efficient methods such as the *von Patera process*, in which silver chloride was made by heating the ore with 7% rock salt and then leached out with sodium hyposulphite solution (a similar reaction to that used to 'fix' photographic materials).

The method of extracting silver by *cyanidation*, which replaced the von Patera process, is essentially the same as that used for GOLD. The silver ore is dissolved by a dilute solution of sodium cyanide in the presence of air, the solution filtered and the metal reprecipitated by the addition of zinc dust:

$$Ag_2S + 4NaCN + 2O_2 \longrightarrow 2NaAg(CN)_2 + Na_2SO_4$$

argentite   sodium cyanide   oxygen (from air)   sodium argentocyanide   sodium sulphate

$$2NaAg(CN)_2 + Zn \longrightarrow Na_2Zn(CN)_4 + 2Ag$$

sodium argentocyanide   zinc dust   sodium zinc cyanide   silver

Most of the base metals such as copper and nickel which are purified by electrolytic methods (see ELECTROLYSIS) contain silver as an impurity. Generally silver is not soluble in the electrolyte and is a constituent of the anode slimes along with gold, platinum and other precious metals. The slimes are collected and subjected to roasting, leaching and smelting in order to remove as much of the base metal (which is now the impurity) as possible. It is then cast into anode blocks and the silver which it contains electrodeposited in a bath of silver nitrate solution on to cathodes of either carbon or pure silver. The silver produced in this way assays better than 999 fine (99.9% pure). The other precious metals are collected as yet another anode slime.

BASF

Top left: checking the weight of silver bullion bars.

Centre left: high purity silver is made by electrorefining. The picture shows impure silver being cast into an anode for the refining process.

Bottom left: examples of hand-made silverwork. The crucifix and candelabra were made in Salzburg at the end of the 16th century, and show the great malleability and ductility of silver.

Right: a catalyst made of silver deposited on an asbestos base. It is used to promote the oxidation of methanol to give formaldehyde, an important industrial raw material.

Lead ores are an important source of silver, which is removed from the smelted lead bullion by liquid phase partition into molten zinc by a method known as the *Parkes process*.

Properties and uses

Silver is unique in that it combines the highest thermal conductivity of any metal with the highest electrical conductivity. Its excellent thermal conductivity (34% better than copper) is familiar to anyone who has stirred a hot cup of tea with a solid silver spoon; and the fact that it is the best conductor of electricity (but only 5% better than copper) commends its use in some special circumstances, for example for coating wires carrying high frequency currents which only flow in the surface layers. Its use for electrical contacts derives more from the properties of the thin layers of oxides and sulphides which form on its surface (they are able to prevent the contacts sticking, but are thin enough to have negligible resistance) than from its high conductivity.

The brilliant shine which silver takes has endeared it to men down the ages. Solid silver, as used for cutlery and ornaments, is never completely pure as it would be too soft, and it is usually mixed with 5% copper to form the alloy known as sterling silver. In jewellery the copper content can be as high as 20%. Base metals can be electroplated with silver, as in EPNS (electroplated nickel silver) ware, in which an alloy of copper and nickel called *nickel silver* is plated with a thin layer of silver. Before the advent of the electroplating technique in 1840, an alternative method of plating was used in which a copper block was heated and pressed between two silver plates so that two pressure welds were formed. The complete sandwich could then be rolled down to any desired thickness, the product being known as *Sheffield plate*.

Silver tarnishes by the formation of a thin surface layer of silver sulphide as the metal reacts with small quantities of sulphur pollutants in the atmosphere. The tarnish can be removed with a suitable metal polish, by an electrolytic technique or by dipping the article in a dilute solution of tin chloride; or on the other hand it can be prevented by thinly electroplating the silver with rhodium (see PLATINUM METALS).

Another application which utilizes the high reflectivity of silver is in the coating of mirrors. The surface to be treated is immersed in a mixed solution of silver nitrate, $AgNO_3$, and ammonium hydroxide, NH_4OH, and the silver is precipitated out on to the glass by adding a suitable reducing agent.

Traditionally silver is used for coinage, but today no major nation still puts the metal in its 'silver' coins. In Britain for example, the silver content of coins was reduced from 92.5% to 50% after World War 1 and to zero after World War 2. Most 'silver' coins are now an alloy of copper and nickel.

Silver solder is an alloy of 30% copper and 10% zinc in silver. It has a high melting point (for a solder) of 770°C (1418°F) and considerable strength. It is used in high quality engineering work and the jewellery industry.

Photography

The most important user of silver compounds is the photographic industry, which consumes thousands of tons annually as chloride and bromide salts, $AgCl$ and $AgBr$ respectively. A photographic image is made up of myriads of minute crystals of silver. These are precipitated from the halide salt during development to an extent dependent on the amount of light to which the salt has been previously exposed. Development is a reduction reaction (see OXIDATION AND REDUCTION), and can be represented as follows (the developer in this case is *hydroquinone*):

$$2AgBr + HOC_6H_4OH \rightarrow 2Ag + 2HBr + OC_6H_4O$$

activated silver bromide   hydroquinone   silver   hydrogen bromide   quinone

In practice, the acid hydrogen bromide which is formed in this reaction is neutralized as soon as it is formed by an alkali such as sodium carbonate, Na_2CO_3, present in the developer solution. After development the image must be 'fixed' and this involves removing the excess silver bromide which was not activated by light during exposure. This is usually done by treatment with a *thiosulphate* salt such as ammonium thiosulphate, $(NH_4)_2S_2O_3$, which forms a soluble complex:

$$AgBr + 2S_2O_3^{--} \longrightarrow Ag(S_2O_3)_2^{---} + Br^-$$

silver bromide   thiosulphate ion   silver-thiosulphate complex ion   bromide ion

SINE WAVE

The sine wave is a very important wave shape used extensively by both scientists and engineers. It is the waveshape observed in the *simple harmonic motion* executed by such devices as PENDULUMS and OSCILLATORS. Also it is closely associated with the properties of a circle and right angled triangles situated within a circle from which the sine and cosine of an angle can be determined (see MATHEMATICS).

A quality or property of something that alternates in the manner of a sine wave is said to be *sinusoidal*. The prongs of a tuning fork oscillate with sinusoidal motion, and the voltage waveform of the household mains supply is sinusoidal.

From circular to linear motion

The piston on a steam locomotive moves backwards and forwards with near-sinusoidal motion because the piston is linked to the perimeter of the drive wheel. With the train travelling at constant speed, the piston undergoes reciprocal motion—speeding towards its central position, overshooting and slowing down as it reaches the end, reversing and speeding back towards the centre again, and so on.

Consider a wheel and piston arrangement with a pen attached to the piston and touching a roll of paper that moves, via gears, according to the motion of the wheel. The shape produced on the paper is a sinusoid. With the pivot point on the wheel horizontally to the right of the wheel axis there is no vertical displacement of the pivot and the pen is at the centre of the paper. Turning the wheel anticlockwise moves the pivot upwards and to the left. The pivot and the pen are now displaced above their central positions. The pen recording is therefore a plot of vertical displacement against the angle of turn of the wheel (or distance along the paper). For the first 180° the displacement is above the line and labelled *positive displacement*; from 180° to 360° (completing the circular motion) the pivot is below the line and labelled *negative*.

After a 360° turn the pivot (and the pen) is back where it started and, continuing to turn the wheel, the pen recording waveform is repeated—that is, the basic sine wave shape is repeated. The sine wave is therefore said to be a *periodic function* and the length of one complete sine wave as measured on the paper is called the *wavelength*.

If the wheel is set spinning at constant speed the pen is said to be moving with *simple harmonic motion*. If the wheel is spinning at 10 revolutions per second (10 rps) then there are 10 repetitions of the basic sine wave shape per second. The *frequency of oscillation* of the pen is then 10 cycles per second—usually written as 10 hertz (10 Hz).

Sine and cosine functions

Mathematicians have given the sine wave its own function which labels and describes its shape—this is the *sine function*. If the pivot on the wheel is displaced by θ from its original (zero displacement) position then its vertical displacement is $\sin \theta$ (assuming that the wheel has unit radius—for example, one metre).

Plotting $\sin \theta$ on the vertical axis of a graph against increasing values of θ (horizontally) produces a sine wave. The cosine of an angle $\theta°$, $\cos \theta$, produces an identical shape when plotted on a graph but the shape is shifted to the left by 90°; $\sin \theta$ and $\cos \theta$ are therefore complementary functions.

The wave shape of sin and cos functions is repeated every 360° and the maximum displacement from the centreline is equal to the radius of the circle generating them. Although θ is shown here measured in degrees it is more common to express angles in radians. 360° is 2π radians (6.2832 radians).

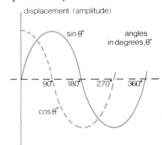

The relationships between sine and cosine functions can be more easily seen from the properties of a right angled triangle—which is where such functions are usually first encountered.

But the full significance of these functions is best demonstrated by placing this triangle inside a circle such that the hypotenuse (r) is a radius of the circle. Then x represents a *horizontal displacement* from the centre of the circle and y the *vertical displacement*.

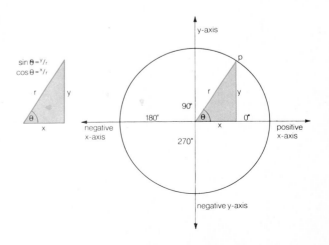

positive displacement

one wavelength

negative displacement

horizontal line through axis of wheel

$\sin \theta = y/r$
$\cos \theta = x/r$

Clearly when $\theta° = 0$, then $y = 0$ and $\sin 0° = 0$, but at this same moment $x = r$ and $\cos 0° = 1$. When $\theta = 90°$, $y = r$ so $\sin 90° = 1$, but $x = 0$, so $\cos 90° = 0$. By suitable labelling of the axes as positive in one direction and negative in the opposite direction, $\sin \theta$ and $\cos \theta$ can be described for angles up to $360°$. So, $\sin 180° = 0$ and $\cos 180° = -1$, $\sin 270° = -1$ and $\cos 270° = 0$ and finally $\sin 360° = \sin 0° = 0$ and $\cos 360° = \cos 0° = 1$. All values in between correspond to the shape of the sine wave.

From Pythagoras' theorem, the sides of a right angled triangle are related by the expression $r^2 = x^2 + y^2$. Dividing both left and right hand sides of this expression by r^2 gives $1 = \left(\frac{x}{r}\right)^2 + \left(\frac{y}{r}\right)^2$. But $\frac{x}{r} = \cos \theta$ and $\frac{y}{r} = \sin \theta$, and so $1 = (\cos \theta)^2 + (\sin \theta)^2$. This expression completely relates the sine and cosine values of an angle $\theta°$.

SIPHON

The word siphon is of Greek origin, and it is almost certainly the Greeks who first made use of the siphon principle for the conveyance of water over long distances. This avoided using open aqueducts, which had to follow the contours of the countryside or alternatively be routed across valleys by means of channels supported on stone arches.

The siphon consists of a tube which is bent to form two legs of unequal length, and can be used to convey liquid over the edge of a vessel and deliver it to a vessel at a lower level. In the case of the Greek water supply siphons, water was transferred over any hump or ridge between the source and the point of required delivery. The small decanting siphon is used by filling the tube with the liquid to be decanted and plunging the shorter leg into the liquid to be drawn. The action of the siphon depends on the difference in pressure in the liquid at the extremities of the tube. The flow is towards the lower level, and ceases when the level within the source and the delivery vessel coincide.

Pressure differences   A simpler way of understanding how the device operates is to consider the pressure in the liquid at each side of the bend at the highest point of the siphon. On the side with the shorter leg the pressure will be atmospheric minus a pressure equivalent to the height of the column of

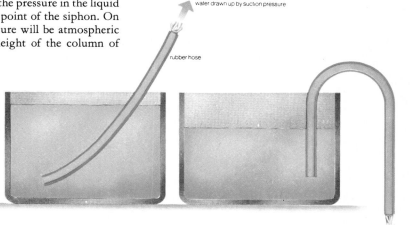

water drawn up by suction pressure

rubber hose

water flowing out at lower level

Above right: siphons are used in home winemaking to draw off the wine from the large bottle without disturbing the sediment which settles at the bottom. This siphon tube is made of clear plastic.

Right: to siphon water from a tank, a rubber tube is filled with water. One end is held closed and the other remains in the water, then the closed end is held below the level of the bottom of the tank. When the water is allowed to flow from the lower end of the tube, the water in the tank is drawn out through the rubber tube by siphon action.

liquid in that leg. On the other side of the bend the same applies but the height of the column of liquid is obviously greater (and the resulting pressure lower) and flow must take place from the higher to the lower pressure. It should be noted that the shorter leg length must not be greater than the height of liquid that atmospheric pressure can support (approximately 30 feet, 9 m, for water) for there is no way that the liquid can be made to rise higher without pumping.

Siphons can be of any physical size, from the glass laboratory device up to water mains pipes of 0.5 m (20 in) diameter or more. The large varieties must, however, have a vent or stop cock at the highest point in order to bleed out trapped air. It should be noted that a pipeline which crosses several ridges and valleys can have very large differences between the pressure of the liquid at the highest and lowest points, and therefore must be built with very much thicker sections in the valleys.

A good example of the application of the siphon principle is in the modern flushing lavatory cistern. The handle is linked to a piston inside the short leg of a siphon, and as the piston is pulled up it fills this leg with water. Once the level of water reaches the high point and starts flowing down the long leg, the siphon is complete. Water continues to flow until the cistern is empty, and at this point the short leg draws air and destroys the effect. The common aerated mineral water siphon is not strictly a siphon at all, as gas pressure is used to expel the liquid.

Below : an old siphon action coffeemaker. Water and ground coffee in the right hand jar were heated by the oil burner beneath it. As the coffee brewed, pressure built up which forced it up the tube, forming a siphon effect which drew it into the glass jar.

SIREN

The siren is a device for the production of audible frequency SOUND waves by the regular interruption of a jet of compressed gas or vapour. It was originally designed for the measurement of audible frequencies by comparison, but is used today as a high volume sound signal. Its name originates from the sea nymphs of Greek mythology, and was given after it was found that the siren would produce sound effectively while operating underwater.

Early types Invented around the beginning of the 19th century, the siren was first used for comparison with sounds whose frequency was to be determined. In its original form it consisted of a flat disc around the edge of which were a series of equally spaced holes. As the disc was rotated a jet of air was directed in line with the holes, so producing a series of air pulses, the audible frequency so generated being directly proportional to the speed of rotation of the disc. An example of this would be a disc with 10 holes rotating at a speed of 15 revolutions every second which would produce an audible frequency of 10 × 15 = 150 cycles per second. By varying the speed of rotation of the disc until it produced the same note as that with which it was to be compared, a fairly accurate value for the unknown frequency could be obtained.

Modern designs Towards the middle of the 19th century, the siren underwent a fundamental change in form which produced the basis of the device in general use today. Instead of the holes being arranged around a flat disc, they were equally spaced around the side of a rotating cup known as a *rotor*. This cup was then placed within a further cup with holes similarly placed to those in the rotor. This second cup remained

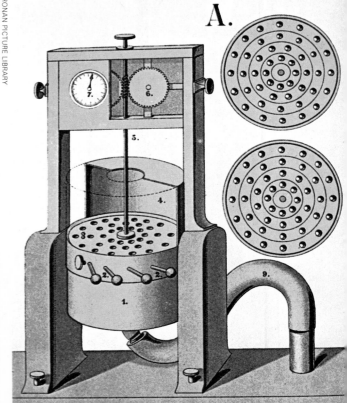

stationary and was known as the *stator*. A jet of air entered the rotor at the open end and was expelled in multiple jets every time the holes in the rotor and stator become aligned. By this method, the level of sound produced was considerably increased because of the increased air pressure changes resulting from the multiple air outlets. The siren thus became a sound signal rather than just a measuring instrument.

The modern siren may either be a device driven by compressed air or steam which is forced into a rotor with angled vanes that cause the rotor to turn under the influence of the compressed air or steam—or, as is more usual, an electric motor drives a rotor with vanes attached which cause air to be sucked in at the front of the rotor, compressed and expelled through the holes in the rotor and stator when these are aligned. The electrically driven siren has the advantage over the compressed air or steam type in that it may be situated in any location where an electricity supply is available, whereas the former type requires a ready supply of air or steam.

The air or steam driven siren is usually a large device, but the electric motor driven versions range in size from very small units powered by a small battery and having an audible range of a few tens of yards to very large units which when mounted on the tops of buildings have a range of several miles.

Below left: picture of siren (1882). At the base is a cylindrical wind chest into which air is pumped. Top surface of chest is studded with regular pattern of holes. Over this is mounted an identical disc which can rotate freely—the holes are slanted so that escaping air causes rotation. The dials record the number of revolutions. Below: a high powered wailing police siren, electrically operated.

SKI

Before World War 2, skis were of solid wood, usually hickory or ash, and up to 8 ft (244 cm) in length—much longer than those of today. They were adequate for the prevailing conditions of predominantly straight running over uncrowded, mainly soft snow, on slopes where turning was largely confined to negotiating corners. Such skis had bare wooden soles on which one applied wax daily with a hot iron. If they had edges at all they were of a composition material limited to the most wearing parts; even after World War 2 one bought steel edges separately in strips and had them screwed on.

The post-war era saw a revolution in ski-ing, not only in the numbers participating but in technique, particularly in the craze for constant turning, leading to the creation of *pistes* (tracks) and bumps (now called *moguls*) on the steeper slopes. The old over-flexible wood skis were inadequate for the changed conditions. Solid wood gave way to wood laminations, then to metal, primitive at first, until finally, in the early 60s, the first epoxy skis appeared. Today, skis have become fine precision tools. They may be loosely divided into wood, metal and fibreglass or, where the last two materials are combined, 'compound' skis. Cross-country skis, used mainly in Scandinavia for touring, rather than fast downhill ski-ing, are similar to the old type: longer, narrower and lighter than downhill skis, of wooden construction without steel edges, and with different bindings (see SKI BINDING).

Below: there are two main methods of ski construction, sandwich and torsion box. In this torsion box type sheets of glass fibre are wrapped around a wood core.

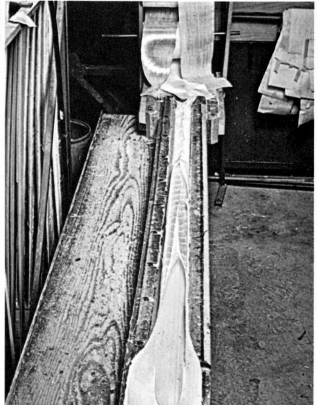

KLAXON LTD

DYNAMIC SKIS LTD

Modern skis

Wooden skis are still found in the lowest price ranges, and consist of wood laminations covered with plastic. Most have plastic running soles and integral one-piece steel edges. Wood has good damping (vibration resisting) qualities but is vulnerable to breakage, warping and fatigue.

Metal skis are not made solely of metal, but are built on a sandwich principle with metal sheets and plastic sidewalls enclosing an inner core of wood laminations or, more recently, polyurethane foam. Of the materials used in skis, metal is the most subject to vibration, which can lead to 'chatter' unless damped by neoprene rubber inserts. These skis have a long life and are at their most popular for powder snow ski-ing.

Glass fibre skis may be built on the same *sandwich* principle as metal skis. Glass fibre has good damping qualities and is particularly suited to piste ski-ing.

In practice nowadays, the combination of metal and glass fibre in varying processes with foam cores and other laminates, making up the *compound* ski, renders the oversimplified distinctions mentioned above less valid than previously. As regards the core, quality light wood has become increasingly expensive and scarce, while polyurethane foam is both easier and cheaper to produce. It is lighter and more consistent, and so enables the manufacturer to reduce production variations. It also has excellent damping qualities and, though less torsionally rigid than wood, cannot warp.

Anatomy of a ski

The top end of a ski is known as the *tip*. Below, where it widens out, is the *shovel*. The *waist* is the narrowest part near the middle. The wider part at the bottom is the *tail*, and the very bottom the *heel*.

A ski may be flexible or stiff overall or it may be soft in front (the degree of *foreflex*) and stiff behind (*aftflex*); a whole range of variations can be achieved with modern materials. The way a manufacturer achieves his desired flex is known as the *flex pattern*. A soft ski will be easier to turn and better for light skiers; a stiff one better for straight running (*tracking*) and the heavyweight.

A ski has a built-in arch (*camber*) in order that the skier's weight may be distributed along the whole length. The camber also provides a springboard effect to assist in *unweighting* (lifting) the skis for turning. Too much camber will make turning hard work; too little will lead to the extremities not getting a grip and slipping. The degree of camber can be seen when the skis are held with their running surfaces together. Because flexibility can now be closely controlled in manufacture, modern skis have a relatively low camber compared to earlier ones, which makes for easier ski-ing.

The degree to which a ski is waisted in relation to the shovel and tail, and the position of the waist, are known as the *sidecut*. When the ski is laid on its edge by knee movement, the tip of a ski with considerable sidecut will bite and turn more than that of a 'non-waisted' ski that has little sidecut. A ski with parallel sides might be ideal for running straight but would have no capacity for turning. A narrow waisted ski favours short sharp turns as in *slalom* (zigzagging between poles laid out on a course). A less pronounced sidecut is better for speed and long turns.

Torsion is the degree to which a ski will twist along its length. If it has a low resistance to twisting, it will not hold too well on icy slopes but will be more forgiving to imperfect techniques. Slalom skis are the most resistant, but if a ski is too torsionally stiff it will judder and vibrate in a turn and lose contact with the snow.

DYNAMIC SKIS LTD

Left: strong epoxy resins are used to impregnate the glass fibre, bonding it to the wood core to form a longitudinal 'box' which is strong and flexible. The 'box' is placed in a mould and the ski put into a hydraulic press.

Top right: before receiving its final lacquer, the ski undergoes sanding and polishing.

Right: cross sections of four types of ski in different price ranges. The simple laminated wood ski was universal only two decades ago, but is now considered to be suitable only for beginners and children. The second, 'sandwich' type ski is a glass fibre reinforced type, but the construction is also used for metal reinforced skis, or for a combination of the two materials. The third ski is a foam injected type, with a toothed 'anchor' edge to give a good bond with the foam. The fourth ski has a torsion box made by the 'wet layup' process.

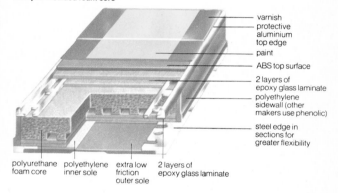

low priced laminated wood ski
- polyurethane varnish
- polyurethane painted with screen printed decoration
- wood laminations
- plain steel edge
- polyethylene sole

ALLARD GRAPHIC ARTS

high quality glass fibre sandwich ski with pre-moulded foam core
- varnish
- protective aluminium top edge
- paint
- ABS top surface
- 2 layers of epoxy glass laminate
- polyethylene sidewall (other makers use phenolic)
- steel edge in sections for greater flexibility

polyurethane foam core | polyethylene inner sole | extra low friction outer sole | 2 layers of epoxy glass laminate

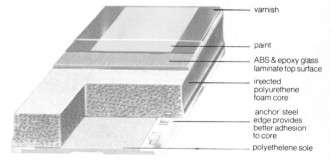

lower priced foam injected ski
- varnish
- paint
- ABS & epoxy glass laminate top surface
- injected polyurethene foam core
- anchor' steel edge provides better adhesion to core
- polyethelene sole

Only a little can be learned by flexing a ski in a shop, because it is the flex pattern taken in conjunction with the degree of camber, sidecut and torsion which make up the dynamics of a ski and determine how it will perform on the snow.

A ski has a *groove* down the centre of the sole; without this, it would be unmanageable in running straight. A very deep groove would be excellent for tracking but would resist turning, so a compromise has to be made. A shallow, rounded groove sacrifices some stability for easy turning and is good for novices. A square cut one favours the faster skier.

Most *running soles* are now made of polyethylene, a low friction material requiring little waxing. Steel *edges* are almost invariably an integral part of the ski, L-shaped in cross-section and fitted in one piece. They may be continuous or segmented, which gives greater flexibility.

Most skiers are using shorter skis than they did a few years ago, and many are opting for 'short' skis below head height. Short skis are lighter and less tiring, easier to turn, slower and therefore less alarming to beginners and, because they exert less leverage in a fall, safer. Above moderate speeds, however, some stability will be lost.

Ski construction
Early laminated skis were made simply by bonding the laminations together, shaping them, screwing metal edges to the sides of the base, applying the sole in the form of a lacquer and painting the top.

Nowadays, however, with more than 20 manufacturers vying for business in a competitive market, there are several methods of construction, each with claimed merits. Vast amounts of money are spent in research and technology. Even for the smallest manufacturer, a press, which is a necessity in

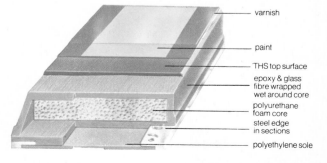

glass fibre torsion box ski
- varnish
- paint
- THS top surface
- epoxy & glass fibre wrapped wet around core
- polyurethane foam core
- steel edge in sections
- polyethylene sole

the construction of all skis, will cost at least £8000 [$18,000].

The most widely used construction is the *sandwich* type. Sheets of metal or glass fibre, or both, are laid over and under the core. The thickness of the sandwich from top to bottom determines the flex pattern, a thin sandwich making for a softer overall flex.

Wood cores are made for preference from hickory or okoumé (a kind of Gaboon mahogany). The lamination strips are bonded vertically to provide torsional rigidity.

Foam cores may be premoulded and have the sandwich materials added, or the foam may be injected into a mould in which the sandwich sheets are already in place. Better bonding can be effected by the first method, but two separately shaped moulds are necessary and thus the process is expensive.

It is more difficult to bond to foam than wood. The strongest epoxy ADHESIVES are used, and often a thin rubber sheet is inserted between the sandwich sheets and the core to allow for the different coefficients of expansion of the materials.

Metal sandwich sheets are of 'Zicral', a very light and strong alloy used extensively in the aeronautical industry. The glass fibre is in the form of unidirectional woven fabric, applied to the mould either soaked in epoxy resin—a messy operation known as wet layup—or in semi-precured sheets, known as 'prepreg'. The wet method gives a better bond with the core; 'prepreg' is commonly used for foam injected skis.

Glass fibre usually provides greater sensitivity and liveliness in a ski than metal, at the expense of some durability. Skis of a compound construction of both glass and metal go some way towards finding the balance.

The other main method of construction used extensively is the *torsion box*. A pre-moulded wood or foam core has wet glass fibre wrapped completely round it to form a longitudinal box. This construction, though slow and costly, ensures high torsional rigidity, imperviousness and durability. Torsion can be varied at any point along the length of the ski by altering the thickness of the box. A sandwich ski has an equal torsion along its whole length.

The base edges are often added as an integral part of a sandwich construction. Otherwise they are laid in place in the press, or taped to the core beforehand. They are made of flexible steel: advanced skis have a softer type that is easier to hone to the razor-sharp edge necessary for precision ski-ing.

The sole, made from polyethylene sheet, is bonded to the underlying sheets. The top surface is generally a sheet of ABS or phenolic PLASTIC, the former being less brittle, the latter providing better damping. The sidewalls are strips of phenolic, except in injected foam skis, where the expanded polyurethane extends to the edge.

When all the components have been put together, the rough ski is put into the press, where it will stay for between 10 and 45 minutes depending on the type of construction and bond requirements. A pressure of between 5 and 45 tons is applied hydraulically. The ski is then removed and passes through the finishing stages of screen printing with a design, varnishing and polishing.

Top right: testing the torsional resistance of a ski, which is vital for accurate control in turning. The front and rear of each ski is tested separately with this strain gauge.

Right: this machine tests the absolute strength of a ski. Modern skis are virtually unbreakable in normal use, unlike the early wooden type, which often broke.

SKI BINDING

The purpose of a ski binding is to keep the skier's boot firmly located on the SKI, allowing the ski to be accurately controlled. Most modern bindings are *safety* bindings, which can be adjusted to come undone when the pull on them exceeds a certain limit. The leverage exerted by a ski on a skier's leg during a fall is considerable, so safety bindings are vital to prevent broken bones and torn ligaments.

History The earliest bindings, found on prehistoric skis preserved in Scandinavian peat bogs, were simple leather straps fastening the skier's toe to the ski. At this time, the ski was purely a form of transport, and it was necessary for the skier's heel to be able to rise to allow him to perform the characteristic running motion of cross-country ski-ing.

By the early years of this century, the standard binding consisted of two upright *toe irons* (flanges on either side of the boot toe) linked by a leather strap over the top to hold the boot in—and a loop of *spring cable* clipped to the ski in front of the toe, passing through *sideguides* on the sides of the ski under the ball of the foot and around a horizontal groove cut across the heel of the boot (or around the indentation between the upper and heel of the boot). The slight stretchiness of the cable allowed the skier's heel to rise; in fact, he could kneel on one ski, which was necessary for performing the then fashionable 'Telemark swing' turn. The degree of 'give' in the binding made it reasonably safe.

Racing skiers, however, needed more rigid location of the ski, and the 'Kandahar' type binding was developed. The toe irons were hooked over the welt of the boot toe, making the strap unnecessary and improving rigidity. Two further sideguides were added behind the original ones, so that the skier's

heel was held firmly down. The only way this type of binding could undo in a fall was by the screws coming out of the ski, so it was dangerous.

The first safety modification was to make the cable clip release the cable if stressed, so that the skier's heel could rise if he fell forward. The original cable clip had been an *over-centre* one, that is, a lever which tightened the cable as it was moved forward and finally locked it when it was moved past the centre point. This clip was now mounted on a coil spring, so that stress allowed it to be pulled backwards. After a certain (adjustable) travel, the clip hit a projection, forcing it open.

Sideways, twisting falls would not open the binding, so the next development was the safety toepiece. In one of its earliest forms, the original 'Marker' toepiece, a triangular piece of metal was mounted on a vertical pivot, so that it swivelled horizontally. The base of the triangle, towards the rear, rested against the square toe of the boot. It had a flange resting above the boot welt and two lugs fitting into small nicks in the edge of the welt to hold the boot in place. A side stress on the boot toe would force the base of the triangle sideways, making the whole toepiece revolve so that the boot toe came out of it. The boot had to move backwards to do this, so that the cable release generally opened as well.

Left: the toe- and heelpiece of a simple step-in binding. The toepiece releases the boot sideways, for twisting falls, and the heelpiece upwards, for forward falls. In addition the heelpiece can slide back against the spring, to allow the spring tension (and hence the ease of release) to be adjusted. This allows the boot to move backwards a little, as it would when it was twisting free of the toepiece, though backward movement does not cause the heelpiece to release.

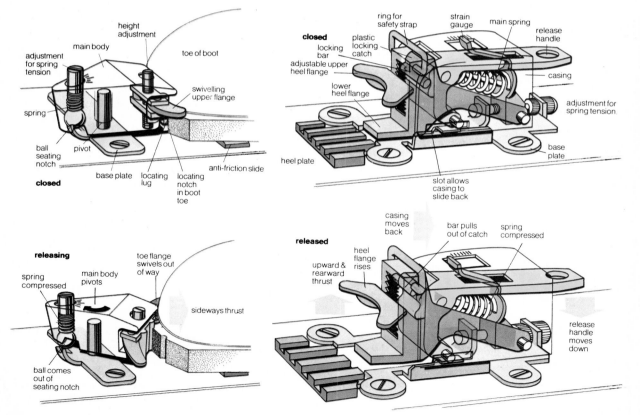

OSBORNE/MARKS

SPECTRUM

P F HANCOCK

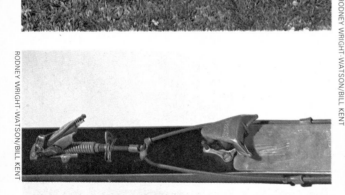

RODNEY WRIGHT-WATSON/BILL KENT

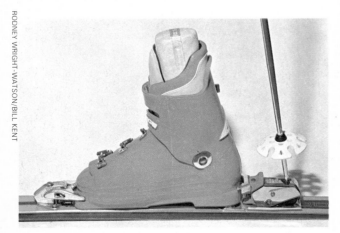

RODNEY WRIGHT-WATSON/BILL KENT

Modern bindings

The old cable binding was prone to jamming through icing up, and a knock on the sideguides could bend them so that they trapped the cable. Modern bindings are mostly of the *step-in* type. The toepiece is often similar to the Marker type. The heelpiece has flanges both above and below the projecting boot heel. In the simpler types, it can release upwards but not sideways. To do up one of these bindings, the toe of the boot is inserted under the flange of the toepiece and the heel lowered on to the bottom flange of the heelpiece. This pushes the heelpiece down and brings the top flange forward to fit over the heel. The binding then clicks shut. It can be released by pushing a lever at the back.

Left: bindings dating from the early years of this century. They have toe irons in which the boot is held by a leather strap over the top, and a leather strap, rather than a spring cable, for the heel. The two pairs on the left are fastened by closing metal catches, but the right-hand pair has to be buckled on. The next picture shows a recent cross-country ski, with flanges on the toe piece to hold the boot, and an inextensible cable on a spring on the front clip.

Left below: an early cable-type safety binding. The clip looks similar to that above, but this one comes undone when the cable is pulled hard. The toepiece is a 'Marker' type, which releases the toe of the boot sideways in a twisting fall.
Bottom: a modern step-in binding, giving the same forward and sideways release, but with greater reliability. Pressing the heelpiece with the point of a ski stick as shown opens it.

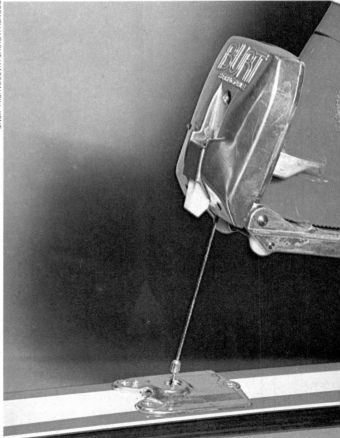

RODNEY WRIGHT-WATSON/BILL KENT

Firmer location of boot to ski is provided by another type of heelpiece sometimes called *latch-in* or (confusingly) *cable*. This has very short cables or rods leading from a clip above and behind the heel to a plate or turntable below the heel. It is less convenient to put on than a step-in, since the skier has to bend down to do it up, but since it goes right around the heel, it is much firmer. Some bindings have plates that run the full length of the boot and are released with it; these are called *plate* bindings.

The ultimate step-in binding is probably the 'Eckel Royal'. Both the toepiece and heelpiece open upwards and sideways, allowing them to release in forward, backward, sideways and twisting falls, or any combination of these.

Accessories

The movement of boot against ski during a sideways or twisting release may be impeded by ice under the boot sole, or a layer of packed snow may become wedged between boot and ski so that the binding will not shut fully. Both conditions are dangerous; the first prevents release, the second makes it happen prematurely. It is customary, therefore, to put *anti-friction plates*, *sliders* or *rollers* on the upper surface of the ski. These allow the boot to move sideways more easily, and create a small gap between boot sole and ski top so that snow build-up is not a problem.

All safety bindings must have *safety straps* to keep the ski loosely attached to the boot after release. The ski might otherwise run away downhill, reaching a high speed and possibly causing injury or damage. Safety straps are a legal requirement in many countries.

The 'Lange Burt'

A recent development, the 'Lange Burt' is a safety binding of an entirely new type. The boot is firmly clipped to a plate which is anchored to the ski by spring loaded, retractable cables. A fall causes the cables to pull out, but as soon as the stress is removed, they snap back into place. This feature allows a skier to fall in any way and, if he can land on his feet, simply to ski on without stopping. As an additional safety feature, the boot heel will come away from the plate when the cables are fully unreeled.

One of the major advantages of this design is that it will give, not only in any direction, but also for any kind of pull, however slow. Conventional bindings tend to release more easily if jerked quickly; a slow pull has to build up to a very high, and perhaps dangerous level to release the binding—though some types do have a certain amount of give deliberately built in to allow some movement without coming open.

SKI LIFT (see cable railway)

Below left: close-up of the heel of the 'Lange Burt' retractable binding, showing how stress causes the cable to unreel. There is a similar arrangement at the toe. As soon as the stress is released, the cables retract and the ski snaps back into place. Step-in plate bindings such as this are the latest development in ski bindings.

Below right: a binding testing machine, which ensures that bindings release at the right tension. The binding set up on the rig is a latch-in heelpiece. Heel- and toepieces are tested separately.

SLAUGHTERHOUSE

The origins of animal slaughter are lost in the unrecorded past when man in his evolutionary development became a hunter. Only in comparatively recent times, perhaps 20,000 years ago, did man achieve one of his greatest advances—the domestication of animals for food, after which the slaughtering process became no longer the culmination of a thrilling chase but a calculated operation.

Early methods of slaughtering domestic animals were by strangulation or piercing the brain through the eye-socket with a heated spear. The improvement in keeping quality by bleeding animals thoroughly must soon have become apparent, and other techniques evolved which still survive in the forms of ritual slaughter according to the Jewish and Muslim faiths.

By mediaeval times, slaughtering was becoming an organized industry in western Europe, but up to the 19th century it was conducted on a local basis, the animals being driven on foot from their pastures to the area of consumption.

Large scale slaughterhouses first developed in the US (chiefly Cincinnati and Chicago) and were operated most intensively in the cool autumn and winter months. If the meat had to be shipped any distance, it had to be heavily salted, smoked or dried. Between 1860 and 1880 effective mechanical REFRIGERATION was developed, and this enabled meat to be transported to any part of the world from slaughterhouses in the producing areas.

The slaughtering industry was probably the first to adopt production line methods, and it is said that Henry Ford was inspired by the Chicago 'packing-houses' (see pages 164–165) to apply the technique to his motor factories in Detroit.

Pre-slaughter treatment It is important to the quality of the meat that animals should not be unduly stressed or fatigued prior to slaughter, otherwise the *glycogen* or muscle-sugar is depleted, resulting in lack of acidity in the chilled carcases which favours more rapid bacterial growth (see FOOD PRESERVATION). Care is therefore taken not to excite or abuse the animals during transportation to the slaughterhouse. Sometimes large establishments retain a 'Judas sheep' which is trained to lead reluctant flocks of sheep more easily into the slaughterhouse, but is not itself killed.

A period of rest is desirable between transportation and slaughter during which the livestock are watered and, if necessary, fed. The feeding in the case of pigs can be with a sugar solution which aids rapid replenishment of the glycogen. Livestock so treated are less prone to restlessness or fighting during the pre-slaughter period, so there is a double advantage in doing this.

Stunning Virtually all developed countries now have legislation requiring livestock to be anaesthetized before being killed. This is achieved in a variety of ways, according to the type of animal and the scale of operations.

Cattle, which were formerly roped round the neck and dragged to a ring fixed in the floor, are now led to a *knocking pen* where they are closely confined and can be stunned without danger to the slaughterman. For pigs and sheep a *restrainer* may be employed. This is a conveyer which carries them along without their feet touching the ground. The old pole-axe has now been replaced by the *captive-bolt pistol* which is held against the front of the animal's skull and fires a pointed bolt which penetrates to a depth of about two inches (5.1 cm), the bolt being subsequently withdrawn. After the cattle are stunned they are usually *pithed* by inserting a long rod through the aperture made by the bolt. This is to destroy the brain and

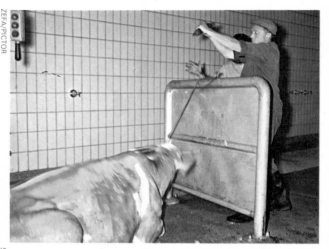

Left: an 18th century French slaughterhouse. Cattle to be slaughtered were tethered to a heavy iron ring fixed to the floor, then the slaughterman hit them with a pole-axe, a heavy axe with a blade on one side of the head and a hammer face on the other side. This method has been replaced by the use of stunning pens which restrict the animals' movements and captive-bolt pistols which fire pointed bolts into the animals' skulls. This makes it safer for the slaughtermen, as there is less risk of being kicked by a struggling animal, and the captive-bolt pistol is more effective and easier to use than the pole-axe.

Above left: stunning a bull with a captive-bolt pistol.

Left: using a power saw to cut a beef carcase.

Above: a black-scraping machine. The singed pig carcases travel through the machine on the overhead conveyer, and the charred skin is scraped off by the steel fingers.

thereby enable subsequent operations to proceed without the danger of reflex muscular action.

Sheep and lambs can also be stunned with the captive-bolt pistol, but where larger numbers are involved, electrical stunning is employed. In this method, electrodes at the end of tongs grip each side of the head and a current of about 80 volts and not less than 250 milliamperes is passed through the brain, causing temporary loss of consciousness without distress.

Pigs are usually stunned electrically, although some large BACON factories employ carbon dioxide tunnels through which the animals are conveyed, inhaling a 70% mixture of the gas which produces temporary unconsciousness.

Killing and dressing Whatever method of stunning is employed, the next stage is to bleed the animal as quickly and completely as possible, by shackling a hind leg, hoisting the animal to a hanging position, and *sticking* it with a very sharp knife so as to sever the main blood vessels of the neck. If the blood is to be used for edible products it may be caught in containers or drawn off from the sticking hole through a hollow knife and a system of vacuum tubes. The blood must be retained in separate batches until all carcases from the batch have been passed fit for human consumption.

From the moment an animal dies, its natural defences against the bacteria which inhabit its digestive tract cease to function, and speed is essential in completing the dressing and cooling of the carcase before these bacteria invade the muscular tissue and begin to multiply rapidly. As some cattle slaughter lines now handle over 250 per hour and pigs can be killed at 1,000 per hour, production line methods are usually employed, with each worker performing his particular job as the carcase passes by. Most of the work is still best done with suitable knives, although power-driven aids are available to help with *flaying* (removing the hide) and cutting off horns and feet.

Pigs are seldom skinned, but are passed through a scalding tank of water at 140°F (60°C) to loosen their hair, and then through a mechanical de-hairer. Those destined for bacon production are then singed for about 15 seconds in a vertical furnace to tenderize and sterilize the rind, after which they are showered and scraped by a *black-scraping machine* with spring-steel fingers to remove the charred outer skin.

Once the hide, fleece, or hair has been removed, the abdominal cavity is opened with a long incision and the *viscera* (stomach and intestines) is removed. Then the chest cavity is opened with a saw-cut through the *sternum* (breastbone) and the liver, heart and lungs are taken out. Next, the beef and bacon-pig carcases are split into two halves down the backbone with power-saws; lamb and pork-pig carcases remain whole. Finally the carcases are weighed and transferred to refrigerated rooms to remove the animal heat.

At various stages the carcases and offals are inspected by qualified meat inspectors for signs of disease which might render the meat unfit for consumption. They are empowered by government regulations to condemn such meat.

Poultry Table birds are slaughtered in specialized packing stations, where they are stunned, bled, scalded and mechanically plucked. A light singeing removes the remaining small feathers, and after *evisceration* (removal of the entrails) the giblets are cleaned in a separate section to be re-packed later inside the trussed carcase. *Spin-chilling* is employed to cool the great number of birds involved. In this process the carcases are tumbled in rotating drums filled with iced water. Most poultry are sold in a frozen state, and the last operation before weighing and packing is to pass them through freezing tunnels.

Ritual slaughter　The *shechita* method of slaughter prescribed under the Jewish religion is broadly similar to the Muslim method, and originates from an early awareness of the need to achieve complete bleeding and the avoidance of ailing animals. No stunning is allowed, and having turned the live animal on to its back (by means of a *casting-pen* in the case of cattle) the *shochet* or cutter recites a prayer before severing the carotid arteries, the jugular veins, the *trachea* (wind-pipe) and the *oesophagus* (food passage) in one clean stroke of a razor-sharp knife. The knife-edge must be absolutely unmarked and the incision completed without pressure or any stabbing movement. If the animal fails to show violent reactions during or after slaughter it is not considered suitable for Jewish food and will not receive the *kosher* seal.

The slaughter of fully conscious animals and the struggling movements which normally follow have led to the banning of ritual slaughter in some European countries. Scientific opinion, however, widely holds that the sudden fall in blood-pressure following the cutting of the throat produces rapid *cerebral anaemia* (lack of blood in the brain), and unconsciousness results within 3 seconds. The violent movements which follow are said to be purely reflex and not a manifestation of agony.

By-products　The by-products of slaughtering are of considerable value both economically and medically. The following list is by no means exhaustive.

Cattle hides are sold to tanneries for LEATHER manufacture.

They may also separate the inner layer which is rich in *collagen*, a gelatinous substance, and this is converted into edible SAUSAGE skins by specialized manufacturers. The hair can be felted and the ear-hair makes fine brushes.

The fleeces from sheep and lambs are sent to *fell-mongers* who convert them into wool and sheepskin, and pigs' hair can be used for paint brushes or curled and rubberized for use in upholstery.

Blood, being rich in proteins, may be consumed in the form of black puddings or dried and incorporated in animal feed and fertilizers.

Hooves, horns and inedible bones are made into glue, while edible-quality bones together with feet produce gelatine. Good quality fat is rendered into lard or dripping, and low grade fat, such as that derived from the gut, can be used in SOAP manufacture.

The small intestines are subjected to a cleaning and salting process which makes them into sausage skins. Ox stomachs are cleaned, bleached and cooked to become edible tripe, and the *thymus* gland is regarded as a delicacy and is called the 'sweetbread'.

The chief pharmaceutical by-products are obtained from various glands. The *pancreas* produces insulin, the *adrenals* give adrenalin, and the *thyroids, pituitaries* and *ovaries* all yield other valuable medicinal products.

SLIDE PROJECTOR (see projector)

Above: unloading offal from a plate freezer. The offal is loaded into the machine where it is formed into frozen blocks. It is then cut into slabs.

Right: a cutting and boning hall where carcases are cut and boned prior to wholesale and retail distribution, or in preparation for further processing into convenience foods such as sausages, pies, and canned meat products. Edible bones can be made into gelatine, which is widely used in photographic materials, glues, and foodstuffs.

SLIDE RULE

The slide rule is an extremely versatile instrument for performing calculations quickly and with reasonable accuracy. It is a cheap instrument compared with its more complicated counterpart—the electronic calculator (see CALCULATING MACHINES) with certain advantages and disadvantages over these machines.

The electronic calculator has the advantage of handling longer numbers, upwards of six digits, whereas the slide rule can only handle up to about four digits. The slide rule is therefore limited in accuracy. Furthermore, with the floating decimal point system, electronic calculators can simultaneously cope with numbers less than a millionth and greater than a million. Slide rules depend on the user to remember the 'scale' of the numbers involved and position the decimal point by reason and skill at the end of a calculation.

Below: the top situation shows how to multiply 3 by 2. The unity mark on the C scale is set against the 2 mark on the D scale. By placing the cursor over the 3 mark on the C scale the answer (6) is found on the D scale. The middle situation shows that the unity mark on the other end of the C scale must sometimes be used. Shown here set against the 5 mark on the D scale, the multiplication of 5 by 3 is found under the cursor on the D scale. The bottom situation demonstrates squares and square roots (using A and D scales); the reciprocal of a number (located on D scale) is found on the C1 scale, showing that the reciprocal of 4 is 0.25.

Slide rules, however, have the advantage that they can handle easily some calculations that only the most expensive calculators otherwise could cope with. Also, they require no battery to power them and they have few parts that can go wrong.

Linear slide rule The most common slide rule is the straight, or linear, version. This consists of two rigidly connected scale sections (like rulers) with an inner scale that can slide. Surrounding this arrangement is a transparent sliding plate with a fine hair line engraved on it perpendicularly across the three sections. This plate—called the *cursor*—can move independently of both the fixed and the sliding parts.

The type of calculation that can be performed on this instrument will ultimately depend on the scales provided but, in general, the following procedure is used where two separate numbers are involved. Firstly, one number is located on the fixed scale and the cursor moved along until the hair line lies directly over this number. Secondly, the reference point on the sliding scale—in multiplication, this will be the 1 (unity) mark—is moved until it also lies directly under the cursor line. Lastly, the second number in the calculation is located on the sliding scale and the cursor moved until it lies directly over this point. The answer is found by determining where this same line crosses the fixed scale.

The most common scales found on slide rules are those used for multiplication and division. These are *logarithmic* in character and multiplication (or division) are performed by

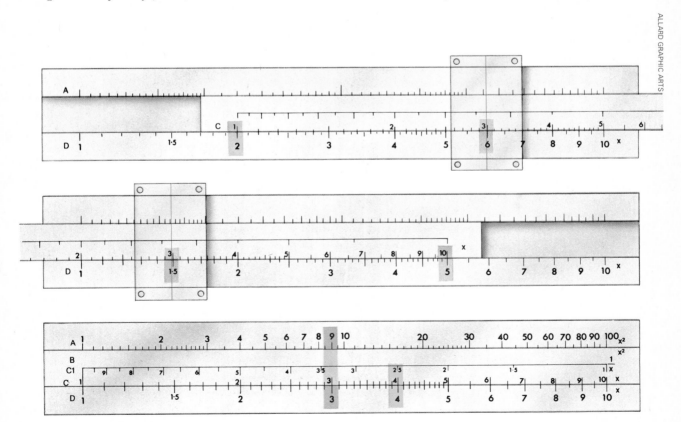

Below: cylindrical slide rule. This can only be used for multiplication and division. The lower end of the black cylindrical cursor is shown set against the number 1.32 on the fixed scale and the top cursor mark against 1.2 on the sliding scale.

Right: two types of circular slide rule. These are light, compact and have the advantage over linear slide rules (shown below right) that calculations cannot 'run off' the end of the scales. Left type shows division of 1.2 (on outermost, D scale) by 1.32 (on adjacent C scale). The result (0.91) is found on D scale opposite '1' mark on C scale. Radial cursor line shown over 1.2 and 1.32 markings.

Below right: the two sides of a general purpose linear slide rule. The C and D scales show the division of 1.2 by 1.32—the answer 0.91 is found on D scale adjacent to '1' mark on C scale. Other scales are also marked. There are two ways of labelling these scales: the alphabetic labels already mentioned (for example, C and D) marked on the left and mathematical notation on the right. The C and D scales are marked x. The AB scales (x^2) are used for obtaining the square of a number (and conversely, square roots). They have two cycles of the basic CD scales but reduced in size. The side shown on the left also has log log scales (six in all) marked on the white fixed sections. Positioning cursor on D scale at $x = 2$ gives value of e^2 on LL3 scale (e^x)—e is the 'natural number', 2.718. Log log scales can be used to find any number to any power.

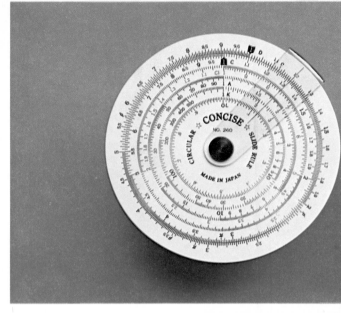

PHOTOS: DAVID KELLY

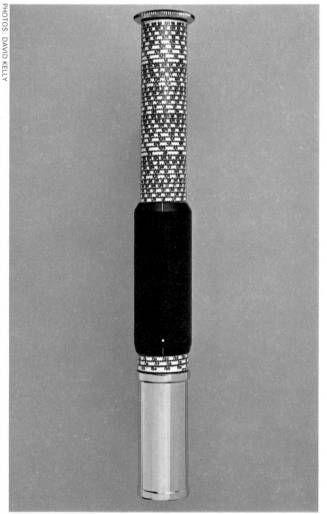

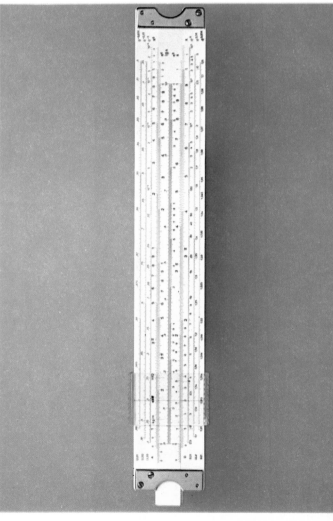

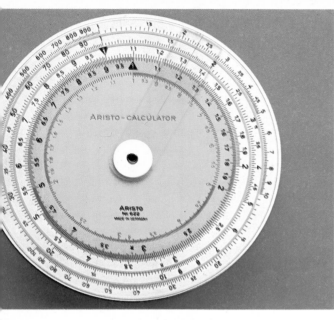

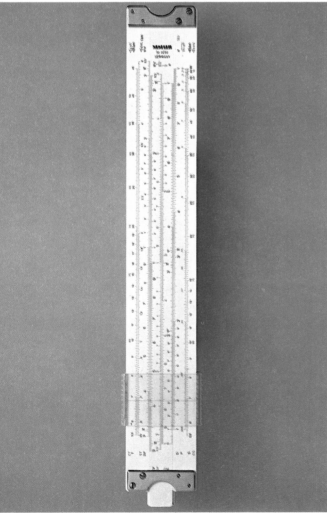

effectively adding (or subtracting) along these scales (see LOGARITHM). Other scales will produce the square of a number, square root, sine, cosine and tangent and the logarithm of a number. Some scales give the constant multiple of a number, and one commonly found is the π (pi) multiple used in calculations involving circles (see MATHEMATICS). Another important scale is the log log scale used for finding the result of any number taken to any power (see LOGARITHM).

Some slide rules will contain all these scales (and more), and this is achieved by making the slide rule two-sided with the cursor line precisely marked on both sides.

Apart from the precision of machining and constructing these instruments (and this is important in all types of slide rule) the accuracy of linear slide rules is limited by their length. The longer the scales, the finer the divisions (graduations) that can be marked. There is, however, a practical limit to the length of linear rules because they are primarily designed to be portable and are usually no more than a foot (30 cm) long. One way of overcoming this limitation is to use a cylindrical slide rule.

Cylindrical slide rule In this, rather than placing the scale in a straight line, it is wrapped in a helix around a tube. In this way, a five foot (1.5 m) scale can be accomodated on a tube two inches (5 cm) long and one inch (2.54 cm) in diameter. The principle behind its design and use is identical to the linear slide rule except that it is 'circularized'. They are, however, more limited because only one type of scale can be incorporated (usually the logarithmic scale for multiplication and division).

The fixed scale is the tubular scale, attached to a handle (for ease of operation). Over this fits a metal tube and at the other end is a sliding scale—a second tube which fits inside and can slide independently of the other two. The metal tube is the cursor with marks at the two rims where the scales project. The technique of cursor-scale manipulations involved in calculations is identical to that of the linear slide rule.

Circular slide rule The logarithmic scale (to the base ten) used in multiplication and division need only be presented between 1 and 10 because other decades (for example, 10 to 100) are identical in form. Because of this cyclical character of the logarithmic scale the slide rule can cope with any number with only one range of scale numbers (1 to 10). For example, to use the number 635 in a calculation one locates instead the number 6.35 (this exists on the slide rule scale) remembering that it is one hundredth of the desired figure.

This cyclical nature of the logarithmic scale makes it ideal for circular slide rules. The scale between 1 and 10 is made to fit exactly into a circle so that the 1 and 10 marks coincide. With circular slide rules, the base disc has the fixed scale marked on it. A second, and smaller, disc turns within the base disc and contains the sliding scale. Over both lies a transparent arm with a radial line engraved—this is the cursor. Unlike a cylindrical slide rule, a circular one may have several concentric scales.

Construction Several factors are taken into account in the design of slide rules. The sliding surfaces must be hard and smooth to prevent wear and permit a smooth and even movement. The material must retain its dimensions—that is, not expand or contract through changes in temperature or humidity. Also, it must be designed to withstand rough handling (as opposed to abuse). The components are commonly made of injection-moulded thermoplastic materials. Some low-priced rules are wooden, with printed paper labels covered in plastic film to protect them.

RONAN PICTURE LIBRARY

MARY EVANS PICTURE LIBRARY

SMEATON, John (1724–92)

Smeaton was among the first to determine the efficiency of the various energy sources of his day, water, wind and steam, demonstrating his conclusions by precisely measured experiments. He was no less renowned as a civil engineer; his masterpiece was the Eddystone lighthouse off Plymouth in the English Channel.

The son of William Smeaton, attorney of Austhorpe near Leeds, John Smeaton was intended for his father's profession, and was sent to study law in London at the age of eighteen. But even as a boy he loved to construct model machines, made his own tools and even built a little steam engine—then quite a novelty—which drained a fish pond in the family's garden. Rather to his father's annoyance, he became so interested in scientific instruments as to bind himself apprentice to an instrument maker. By 1750 he was ready to set up in trade for himself, and soon began to devise improvements to a wide variety of instruments, mainly for navigation. He submitted these to the Royal Society, of which he was elected a Fellow in 1753 at the age of twenty-nine. The next year he visited the Netherlands to study methods of canal and harbour construction there. Soon after his return, his reputation for mathematical and engineering skill earned him the contract to erect a new lighthouse on the Eddystone rocks. Two earlier wooden lighthouses had already been destroyed by fire and storm. He resolved to build a stone structure, despite the immense difficulties of construction work on such a site, and devised a system of dovetailing the stone blocks to provide mutual support.

It took three years to complete the job; Smeaton supervised on the spot with great courage. The new lighthouse stood up to severe gales, and Smeaton's name was made. The year of its completion, 1759, he began his experiments on the power of wind and water to turn mills; this was the first time a prolonged series of tests had been carried out to discover the most efficient form of windmill and waterwheel. Each particular component and element was varied in turn and the result of the alterations carefully measured, so as to arrive at the ideal shape and size of each part, and calculate effects on output. In 1769 he set about doing the same for steam power, studying the efficiency

Above left: Smeaton's apparatus for measuring the power of various designs of windmill. Pulling the rope caused the column and model to turn, creating a breeze from the windmill's point of view. As its sails turned, they wound the weight up the central column, giving an indication of the work done by the design.

Above: Smeaton is regarded as being the first fully professional civil engineer, combining good construction techniques with economy.

of the Newcomen engine. Where Watt, soon after, was to invent a revolutionary new machine, Smeaton sought rather to make existing types more effective, again measuring the variations of each of the parts of the engines then in use.

Meanwhile, he was equally busy as a civil engineer. He designed three segmental arch bridges in Scotland and one, his only failure, in England. Most of the 1760s he spent in Scotland—his family had Scottish connections, and claimed descent from a well-known Scottish reformer. He was consulted on very many projects; harbours, bridges, drainage schemes, and designed much of the machinery of the famous Carron iron works. But his major work there was Scotland's first important canal, the Forth and Clyde, to link up the two estuaries which were the main highways of the country's commerce. Financial problems held work up; although begun in 1768, it was not completed for over twenty years, when Smeaton was well past sixty. In the south, his main undertaking was Ramsgate Harbour in 1774. But he continued his theoretical work and gathered around him in London a group of engineers interested in the development of their profession, nicknamed the 'Smeatonians', the nucleus from which the Institute of Civil Engineers later grew. But his home was always in his family's house at Austhorpe, where he had married; a shy reticent man, his chief diversion was astronomical observation which he found time for by raising his fees to fifty guineas a week to discourage the many clients who hankered after his services.

SMELTING (see under individual metals)

SMOKING (FOOD) (see food processing)

SNO-CAT (see tracked vehicles)

RADIO TIMES HULTON PICTURE LIBRARY

GERARD BROS LTD

Above: boiling soap in 1860.

Right: the technology has changed but not the essentials of the process. Soap is boiled in a steel 'pan' fitted with steam coils. First the fat is pumped in and lye is added slowly over a period of several hours; then brine is used to separate the soap into a curd.

SOAP manufacture

Soaps are salts of mixed fatty acids, and they are prepared mainly by reacting fats with caustic alkali (*saponification*). Alternatively, the fatty acids may be split from the fats and then saponified. The properties of the resultant soap will depend on the mixture of fats (or fatty acids) used, the kind of caustic alkali, and the post-saponification processing the soap undergoes. As an alkali, caustic soda, caustic potash, or mixtures of the two may be used, but commonly it is caustic soda. Potash produces a more readily soluble soap and is reserved for soft soaps and shaving soaps. The fat-caustic reaction can be written thus:

$$\begin{array}{llll}
CH_2COOR & & NaOCOR & CH_2OH \\
| & & + & | \\
CHCOOR' & + \; 3\,NaOH \longrightarrow & NaOCOR' \; + & CHOH \\
| & & + & | \\
CH_2COOR'' & & NaOCOR'' & CH_2OH \\
\text{fat} & \text{caustic soda} & \text{soaps} & \text{glycerine}
\end{array}$$

R, R' and R'' represent organic groups containing only carbon and hydrogen atoms, for example the *palmitic* group, $-C_{15}H_{31}$. Both animal and vegetable fats are used, but many of the marine animal and vegetable fats are too soft to yield usable soaps directly. They must be 'hardened' by a process of selective *hydrogenation* to a more useful state. (Hydrogenation of a fat is the addition of hydrogen atoms to its molecules in the presence of a CATALYST.)

History

The treatment of fat with alkali has been practised in the Middle East for at least 5000 years. The art was brought to Europe by the Phoenicians about 600 BC. Its purpose, right through to the second century AD, was solely medicinal, for example, for the treatment of 'scrofulous sores'. Soapmaking disappeared from Europe with the decline of the Roman Empire. It reappeared in the eighth century, but only reached Britain in the eleventh, probably as a result of the Norman invasion. It remained a relatively primitive art till the sixteenth century, when techniques that provided a purer soap—the conversion of pot ash (literally made from wood ash in an iron pot) to caustic alkali by means of quicklime, and the salting out of soap—were developed. In the seventeenth century Leblanc produced caustic alkali from common salt, and thereby elimi-

nated a major stumbling block to expansion. (Today it is made by an electrolytic process.) In the nineteenth century Chevreul described the constitution of fats and put soapmaking on a sound basis. At the turn of the century Sabatier and Senderen discovered how to hydrogenate unsaturated compounds and Normann applied their ideas to the hardening of fats. In the first half of the twentieth century the crystalline states of hydrated soaps—which affect product performance—were elucidated, the bleaching of fats was perfected, and deodorization of fats was introduced for the highest class products.

Manufacture

Soap may be made either in batches or continuously, but the batch process is now mainly reserved for small scale outputs. In batch working, a molten premixed fat charge is pumped to a steel pan fitted with open and closed steam coils and run-off facilities. The fat is heated with open steam as the caustic solution (*lye*) is added slowly and intermittently over a period of hours. 'Half spent lye' (see below) is pumped in during the early stages to aid emulsification. At the end of saponification, brine is fed in till the soap separates as a curd. The underlying lye, which contains the glycerine, is run off. The soap is washed by boiling it up with a quantity of water and re-salting out. A second lye is removed. There is now a finishing stage to ensure complete saponification. For this, a calculated quantity of caustic is added and the mass is boiled gently for around five hours. More caustic is then added till the soap separates as a loose curd, leaving 'half spent lye'. Finally the soap is 'fitted' by boiling it up and adding brine carefully till it flakes in a particular manner, readily recognized by an expert process worker. On settling—which may take up to four days— it separates in three layers: pure *neat soap* uppermost, next an impure *nigre soap*, and at the bottom a *nigre lye*. The neat soap is skimmed off for further processing. The nigre soap goes to be re-worked. The whole process requires about a week.

By contrast, the more recently introduced continuous process takes only fifteen minutes, but it requires a large throughput to be economic. The sequence of treatment—saponification, salting out, washing and fitting—is the same, but all stages are carried out in totally enclosed vessels. Control is maintained by monitored feed and regulated by FEEDBACK information.

There is a saponification column fitted with stirrers and operated at high pressure and temperature (130°C, 266°F). Fat and caustic are fed in concurrently by proportioning pumps. The saponified mass leaving the column passes to two CENTRIFUGES (or two pairs of duplicates) where it is washed alternately by spent lye and brine to remove the glycerine. The washed soap then enters a fitting column concurrently with a brine and caustic solution, and from there passes to three centrifuges working in parallel, which separate neat soap from nigre. Alternately, the fat may be split and the freed fatty acids purified and reacted directly with caustic or carbonate alkali at a concentration that yields the equivalent of a neat soap.

Types of soap Laundry soaps are made from neat soap, which contains some 28% water. Warm molten soap—dosed if required with perfume and other additives—is splayed over internally cooled drums and scraped off as flakes. These are fed to milling rollers which, by 'working' the material, modify its crystal structure beneficially. The milled flakes pass to a *plodding* machine which not only works the soap further, but also compacts it to bar form. The bars are cut and stamped to their final shape.

Toilet soaps use higher quality fats and the water content is reduced to 10% or less. The neat soap is cooled and flaked as before, but the flakes are passed through a hot air drying oven to reduce the water content prior to milling. Trace constituents are metered in at the milling stage. Since the soap is drier, higher pressures are required here and in subsequent plodding. The emergent plodded bar is cut, stamped and wrapped.

Soap flakes are prepared by a process that is substantially the same as that for toilet soaps up to the milling stage, but the

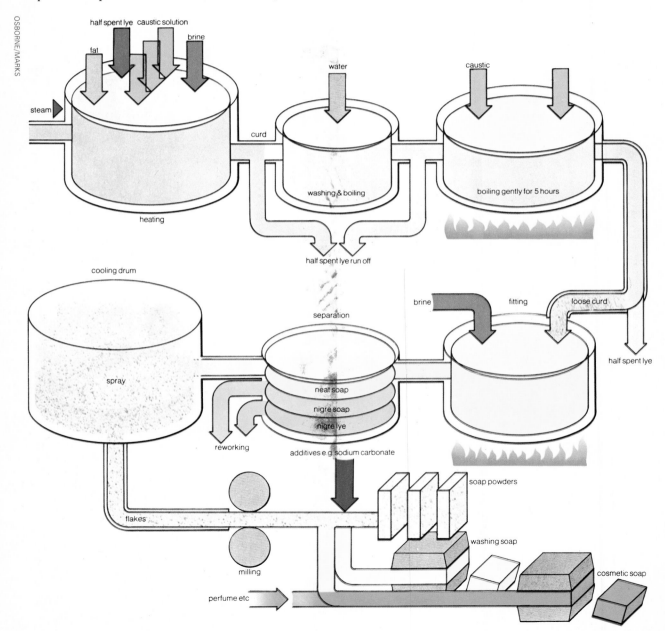

drying stage reduces the water content to about 7%, and the final milling rollers produce a very thin—and hence instantly soluble—flake, and cuts it, if required, to a defined shape.

Soft soaps are made from fats with a high proportion of unsaturated acids (organic acids which contain double bonds in their HYDROCARBON portions), and are saponified with caustic potash. They are made by a 'cold' process in which the only heat involved is that of the reaction, and the glycerine is not removed. The finished product is a translucent solid solution containing either about 45% soap, if for toilet use, or 35% soap, if for domestic cleaning.

Shaving soaps are made from fats with a minimum of unsaturated acids—stearine, tallow and coconut oil—saponified with caustic potash or a potash-soda mixture to promote easy lathering. A cold process may be used, but more likely a 'semi-boiled' process, that is, one on which the initial reaction is promoted by external heating and continued by the heat of reaction. Again, the glycerine is not removed.

Soap powders are formulated products designed to facilitate the removal of fatty and particulate dirt from fabrics with minimum of physical effort. Ancillary constituents deal with chemical stains and general yellowing. Soap provides 50% of the product. The washing aids are sodium carbonate, sodium silicate and sodium tripolyphosphate, but the silicate also helps to produce a readily pourable powder. All are mixed to a paste with molten soap, and the paste is heated and blown under pressure through nozzles to fall as fine particles into a cooling chamber. Minor constituents are metered in as the powder is moved along to the packing machinery. (See also DETERGENT MANUFACTURE.)

Above: the 'fitting' or 'finishing' column in a large modern soap factory. Any free fatty acids left are neutralized here, using an adjusted concentration of caustic and salt.

Right: a giant mincer 'noodling' soap.

Left: the soap-making process. First the solution of fat and caustic soda, together with recirculated lye, is steam heated in brine. The curd is washed and boiled while some of the lye is run off. Then it boils gently for some time, with fresh caustic added. Next the curd gets some more brine treatment; then it is separated into various soap products, some of which need further treatment. Final treatment involves more additives, depending on the final product, and mechanical treatment such as flaking, milling, pressing into cakes, and so on.

SODA FOUNTAIN

The soda fountain, located in an ice cream parlour or drug store, was for several generations common in America, and is still seen in cafes and snack bars in Britain and other countries. *Ice cream sodas* were made with *carbonated water* in a tall glass, so that the melted ice cream at the bottom of the glass was fizzy. Soft drinks were also made with carbonated water. (Soft drinks are also called *pop* or *soda pop* in America, since the days when the bottles were sealed with corks, which made a popping sound when they were pulled out.)

Carbonated water was invented by Joseph Priestley (1733–1804), an English scientist, politician, writer and Unitarian minister. It is a solution of carbon dioxide in water under pressure, and acts as a preservative as well as supplying flavour and fizz. In its early manufacture it was generated from sodium bicarbonate with an acid, and has been called soda water ever since, although it has little to do with soda in the chemical meaning of the word.

Ice cream sodas are rare nowadays because of the dominance of fast-food merchandizing; there is no profit in them any more because it takes too long to make one. The modern equivalent of the soda fountain is the *soft drink dispenser*. These can be either *post-mix* or *pre-mix* machines; coin-operated vending machines which deliver soft drinks can also be of either type. A pre-mix machine has the drink already mixed, while the post-mix machine mixes the drink as it is delivered to the cup.

Post-mix dispensers The typical soft drink dispenser uses a cylinder of carbon dioxide gas which may be at a pressure of as much as 3000 psi (2068 bar), depending on the temperature. The gas is fed to a container of water called the *carbonator*; a

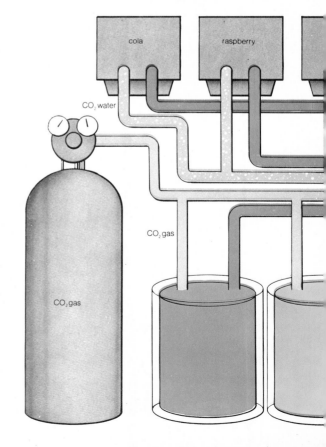

Below left: a soda fountain of the 1890s in America. The taps dispensed carbonated water and the row of containers below dispensed flavours of syrup.

Left: a soda fountain of 1863. Before the unfortunate attempt to prohibit alcoholic beverages in the USA from 1920 to 1933, soda fountains were almost as popular as bars have become today. Perhaps because of their influence, draught beer in America is always dispensed by gas pressure; there is no 'natural' beer.

Below: a diagrammatic representation of a soda fountain. CO_2 gas goes to the carbonator-cooler and the carbonated water is piped to each dispenser. The syrups can also be circulated around the cooler; the gas pressure is used to push the syrups out of their tanks. The same gas pressure could also be used to dispense wines and beers.

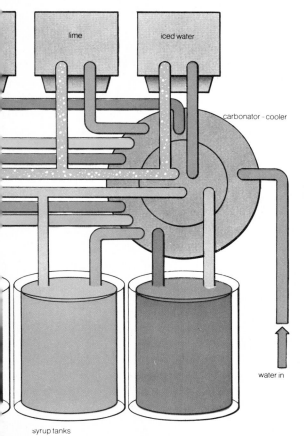

lime

iced water

carbonator - cooler

water in

syrup tanks

regulator on the cylinder lowers the pressure on the gas to about 70 psi (48 bar) and there is a check valve on the delivery side of the carbonator to prevent migration of the gas.

The carbonated water is pumped through the lines of the system through a cooling unit and delivered to the dispensing heads, of which there may be several, each delivering a different flavour of syrup along with the carbonated water. Each dispensing head has an activating lever operating the valves, so that the operator need only push the cup against the lever to operate it, and a nozzle to combine the flow of the two valves, one for the syrup and one for the carbonated water.

Water is available to the carbonator from a pump at a rate of 100 gallons (455 litres) per minute, and another pump delivers the carbonated water to the heads at the same rate. The heads deliver the mixture at a rate of about six drinks per minute. There is a return line for the carbonated water, and if the draw rate exceeds 100 gallons an hour, a system of valves ensures that no warm carbonated water reaches the heads.

Some machines use the pressure of the carbonated gas to push the syrup out of the containers. The cooled carbonated water can be piped around the rest of the system for more efficient cooling, or the cooling machinery may be built into the carbonator to make a HEAT EXCHANGER. Some designs also have filters to clean the incoming water in case it is so heavily treated with chemicals as to affect the taste of the drinks. The dispensing heads can be located up to 300 feet (91 m) away from the rest of the system for convenience, and the delivery lines are made of flexible plastic tubing which can be tucked away under floors, counter tops and so forth. Beers and wines can be dispensed by the same system, using the gas pressure.

SODIUM

Sodium is a silvery white ALKALI METAL which tarnishes rapidly in air, emitting a green phosphorescence (see LUMINESCENCE) visible in the dark. The origin of its chemical symbol, Na, is the Arabic *natrun*, from the Greek word *nitron* which means soda ash (sodium carbonate). The name 'sodium' is simply a Latinization of the word 'soda'. It is extremely light for a metal, having a density of only 0.93 g/cc, and it therefore floats on water, with which it reacts violently to form sodium hydroxide (caustic soda) and hydrogen:

$$2Na + 2H_2O \longrightarrow 2NaOH + H_2$$

sodium   water   sodium   hydrogen
metal   hydroxide

Sodium metal was not isolated until 1807, when Sir Humphry DAVY succeeded in electrolyzing molten caustic soda. Two of its compounds, however, have been used since ancient times. Sodium chloride (common salt, see SALT PRODUCTION) in addition to being necessary to sustain life, has always been employed both to preserve and flavour food. The other important compound is sodium carbonate or soda; it occurs as the mineral *natron*, and has also been prepared by leaching (treating with water) the ashes of plants which grow on the sea shore. The treatment of land plants or deep sea weed in the same way yields a similar compound, which was originally known as mild vegetable alkali or pot ash. This compound is potassium carbonate, K_2CO_3.

In addition to deposits of common salt (NaCl), soda (Na_2CO_3), *borax* (sodium borate, Na_3BO_3) and *Chile saltpetre* (sodium nitrate, $NaNO_3$), sodium is a constituent of many rocks, usually in the form of an aluminosilicate such as a *plagioclase feldspar*.

JAMES BLAKE

JAMES BLAKE

PHOTO : DAVID KELLY

Production In spite of the fact that Davy had first produced sodium by ELECTROLYSIS, early commercial production of the metal did not take advantage of this technique because large quantities of electric power were not economically available. Instead, sodium was prepared by a process devised by Castner in the 1880s, in which caustic soda and carbon in the form of pitch were heated to 1000°C (1832°F) in the presence of spongy iron. The caustic soda was reduced (see OXIDATION AND REDUCTION) by the carbon to metallic sodium. By the 1890s, the technology of electricity generation had advanced sufficiently to encourage Castner to revert to Davy's original method. He designed a cell in which the caustic soda electrolyte was kept at about 10°C (18°F) above its melting point, which was reduced from 318°C (604°F) to less than 300°C (572°F) by adding sodium chloride and sodium carbonate. The sodium is formed on an iron rod *cathode* (negative electrode) which is inserted through the cell base. It floats up through the molten sodium hydroxide and is collected and removed in a ladle. The hydroxyl ions migrate to an annular nickel *anode* (positive electrode) where they are converted into water and oxygen. The water dissolves in the electrolyte and is either electrolyzed in its own right or migrates to the newly formed sodium, with which it reacts. Either way, hydrogen is produced in addition to the sodium, and the maximum yield of the cell reduced by one half. A nickel gauze is inserted between the anode and cathode to prevent sodium diffusing to the anode area, where any water present would result in hydrogen being liberated with the oxygen—a dangerous mixture.

At first sight the production of sodium by the electrolysis of the chloride has many advantages over Castner's method. Sodium chloride can be easily mined or obtained by the evaporation of sea water, whereas sodium hydroxide must be prepared by a technique such as the electrolysis of brine; furthermore no water is produced in the cell, so its maximum theoretical yield is 100%. Neither hydrogen nor oxygen is produced, and the CHLORINE collected at the anode is a valuable by-product. Unfortunately pure sodium chloride melts at 805°C (1481°F) at which temperature sodium metal is relatively volatile (it boils at 877°C, 1611°F), and in addition to this the solubility of sodium in the molten electrolyte is so high as to make the process unworkable. Both these problems can be overcome by adding sodium carbonate to lower the electrolyte melting point to below 600°C (1112°F). Sodium is normally produced from sodium chloride in a *Downs cell*, which is similar to the Castner cell except that the anode is made of carbon and placed centrally and the sodium is formed at an annular iron cathode. Although the current efficiency is twice that of the Castner cell, the Downs cell operates at about twice

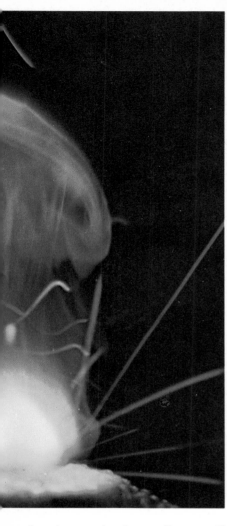

Far left, above: pieces of sodium metal are stored in a jar of paraffin oil. Because sodium is so reactive it must be stored under oil to exclude air, which would rapidly oxidize it to sodium oxide.

Far left, below: a sodium vapour discharge tube. These lamps emit the yellow light characteristic of sodium and they are widely used in the UK for street lighting. The lamps operate at low pressure and high temperature (about 270°C, 518°F). To cut down heat loss and thus improve efficiency, the lamp envelope is mounted in a glass vacuum tube.

Centre left: a piece of sodium placed on a wet surface bursts into flame spontaneously. The metal reacts vigorously with water to produce sodium hydroxide and hydrogen gas, which is ignited by the heat of the reaction.

Near left: the primary pump of the prototype fast reactor at Dounreay, Scotland. The pump circulates liquid sodium through the reactor core in order to remove as rapidly as possible the large amounts of heat generated.

the voltage, so that the overall energy efficiency of the process is no higher. Nevertheless, the ready availability of sodium chloride and the chlorine by-product still weigh in favour of the Downs process, and it is almost universally used.

Uses One of the major uses of sodium is in the production of sodium compounds. Sodium peroxide, Na_2O_2, is made by passing dry air over sodium metal at 300°C (572°F). It is used as a bleach for textiles and also for the production of other bleaches such as benzoyl peroxide $(C_6H_5COO)_2$, which is used to whiten flour. Sodium cyanide, NaCN, is used in huge amounts for the extraction of GOLD, for case hardening steels and in ELECTROPLATING baths. It is prepared in two stages. First, sodium metal is heated in ammonia at 350°C (662°F) to form sodamide, $NaNH_2$, a compound which itself finds application in the dyestuffs industry and in the production of lead azide, $Pb(N_3)_2$, an EXPLOSIVE; next, sodium cyanide is formed by reacting the sodamide with red-hot charcoal. Sodium also plays an important part in the manufacture of sodium alkyl sulphates for detergents. Tetraethyl lead, $Pb(C_2H_5)_4$, the anti-knock constituent of motor fuel, is made by reacting a sodium-lead alloy with ethyl chloride, C_2H_5Cl, and the pure metal is added in concentrations of less than 0·1% to effect the modification of aluminium-silicon alloys.

The high thermal conductivity and thermal capacity of liquid sodium is utilised in the production of valves for high performance internal combustion engines. The valve stems are filled with sodium (see page 659), which greatly enhances the removal of heat from the valve head. This property, combined with a low neutron capture cross section, has led to its use as a heat transfer medium in fast neutron NUCLEAR REACTORS where a large amount of heat must be removed from a small reactor core in the shortest possible time. If desired, the melting point of sodium can be considerably reduced by adding potassium: an alloy of 23% sodium and 77% potassium has a melting point of −12°C (10°F), in other words, like mercury, it is a liquid at room temperature. Such alloys find applications in high temperature thermometers.

Sodium, suitably contained, has also been considered as a conductor for electric power transmission. Its conductivity on a volume basis is only one third that of copper, but in terms of weight it is nearly three times as good. It is also much cheaper.

The familiar yellow sodium street lights have DISCHARGE TUBES filled with sodium vapour. Electrons are continually raised to excited energy states in the atom by the high operating voltage, and they emit monochromatic (one-coloured) light as they drop back to the ground state. The red colour emitted as the light warms up is due to the neon gas with which the tube is filled—a similar effect to a neon light.

SOLAR ENERGY

The Earth receives enormous amounts of radiant energy from the Sun, which directly or indirectly sustains all living things. Anxiety about dwindling supplies of fossil fuels and about the problems that accompany nuclear power (see ENERGY SOURCES) had led to interest rapidly growing in the possible ways of harnessing solar energy in ways useful to man.

Energy available The sun radiates energy at a virtually constant rate of 3.8×10^{20} MW (380 million million million megawatts) by nuclear FUSION processes in its interior, which cause it to lose mass at a rate of some 4 million tons per second. The orbit of the Earth round the Sun is slightly eccentric, so that the solar intensity just outside the atmosphere varies slightly from 1399 MW per square kilometre at the closest (January 3) to 1309 MW per square kilometre at the furthest (July 4). The energy distribution in sunlight as seen outside the Earth's atmosphere approximates fairly closely to a *black body* radiator at 6000°K, but this spectrum is modified as the sunlight passes through the Earth's atmosphere. (A 'black body' is one which absorbs and radiates energy perfectly.) The ultra-violet component is cut down by absorption in the ozone layer at about 30 miles (50 km) altitude, and parts of the infra-red are absorbed by water vapour and carbon dioxide. Moreover, some light is scattered out of the beam by dust particles and molecules of the air. Most of this scattered light reaches the ground in diffuse form, however, and since short wavelength LIGHT is the most strongly scattered, the sky generally appears blue. The extent of all these effects depends on solar altitude and local atmospheric conditions. The *insolation*, or solar intensity, at any point on the Earth's surface therefore varies with the season and the time of day in a regular way, and irregularly with cloud cover. The maximum intensity, of about 1000 MW/km², occurs when the sun is overhead in a clear sky, but average figures are lower than this. Highest annual insolation occurs in the tropical desert areas (near the Equator, insolation is somewhat reduced by high humidity).

The solar energy that falls on the Earth's surface heats the surface of land and water, and evaporates water from rivers and oceans. Only a small proportion (less than 2%) is converted to the mechanical energy of wind and waves and into stored chemical energy in plants by the process of *photosynthesis*. WINDMILLS and other techniques of CONSERVATION TECHNOLOGY can utilize some of this energy, but solar energy as such is not at present harnessed by man in significant quantities. Although the energy falling on the Earth in a fortnight is equivalent to the world's total initial stock of coal, oil and gas, large areas of collectors are required to collect significant amounts of solar energy, and the price of conventional fuels is only just rising to the point at which the capital expenditure on such collectors would be justified.

Solar water heating When solar energy falls on a black object, which absorbs the light, the object is warmed, and in this way radiant energy can be readily transformed into low temperature heat. One of the simplest, as well as the most widespread, applications of solar heat is the provision of domestic hot water, using solar flat plate collectors. Several million of these are in use today, mainly in Japan, Israel and Australia. The units generally consist of a metal plate with a blackened surface, through or over which water flows in pipes or corrugations. The plate is insulated behind to prevent heat loss by conduction, and in front of it there is an air gap of a few centimetres and then one or two glass cover plates, which help to prevent convective heat loss. The collector is placed facing

DAILY TELEGRAPH COLOUR LIBRARY

south (in the northern hemisphere) or north (in the southern hemisphere) at a tilt angle which is usually equal to the angle of latitude, so the collector surface is perpendicular to the average direction of the Sun's rays.

Solar radiation (both direct and diffuse) passes through the glass cover plate and warms the metal surface, which in turn warms the water flowing through the plate. The water is circulated from the hot water storage tank, either by convection or by a small pump. With appropriate THERMOSTAT controls to switch the system off when the insolation is too weak to make a useful contribution, solar water heaters can readily provide a reliable domestic supply of hot water in consistently sunny areas of the world. A conventional booster heater is, however, generally fitted in the tank to provide heat during prolonged cloudy spells.

The average thermal efficiency—the ratio of heat falling on them to useful heat extracted—of these collectors is generally in the region of 45 to 65%. The main heat losses occur from the front surface of the collector itself, provided all other parts of the system are well lagged. The glass cover assists in minimizing these losses, since glass is transparent to visible radiation but opaque to infra-red. Thus, solar radiation passes through it but the long wave thermal radiation from the warm collector plate cannot pass outward through the glass. The system can be made more efficient by means of a vacuum between the glass and the metal plate, so that heat is not lost through conduction or convection through the air (just as a THERMOS FLASK keeps hot), and by using suitable *spectrally selective* surfaces on the metal. These are surfaces with properties opposite to those of glass. They absorb visible radiation efficiently, so they are black to sun-

KEYSTONE PRESS AGENCY

Far left, top: any magnifying glass will concentrate the Sun's rays: this version, of giant proportions, was used in the 18th century by Lavoisier and others to produce very high temperatures for experiments.

Centre: the reflective surfaces of this portable oven focus solar heat at its centre.

Bottom: modern laboratories use parabolic reflectors in the same way as burning glasses to produce high temperatures at low cost. This 'solar furnace' is at the University of New South Wales, Sydney.

Left and above: two views of the French solar furnace at Odeillo in the Pyrenees. 9000 mirrors form a north-facing parabolic reflecting surface with the furnace room at its focus. 11,000 flat mirrors on the hillside opposite can be moved to direct the Sun's rays on to the curved reflector. In minutes, the pollution-free furnace is at 3300°C (6000°F).

OSBORNE/MARKS

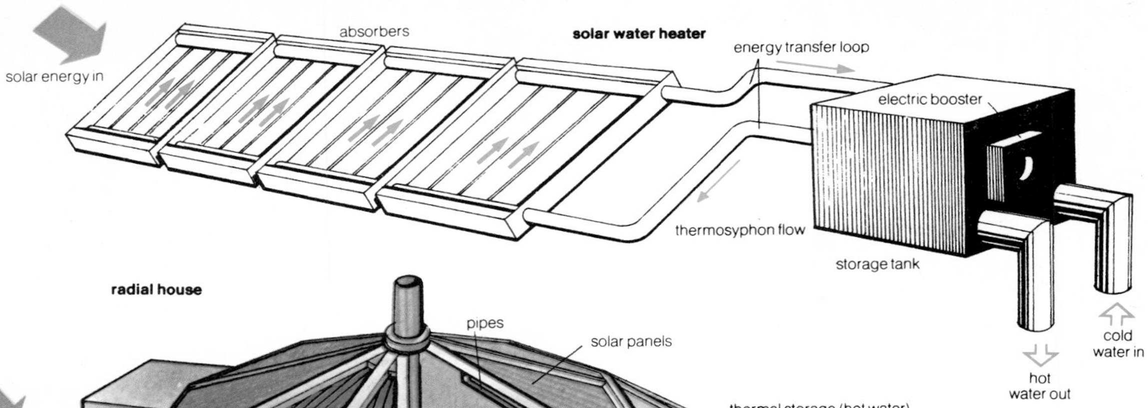

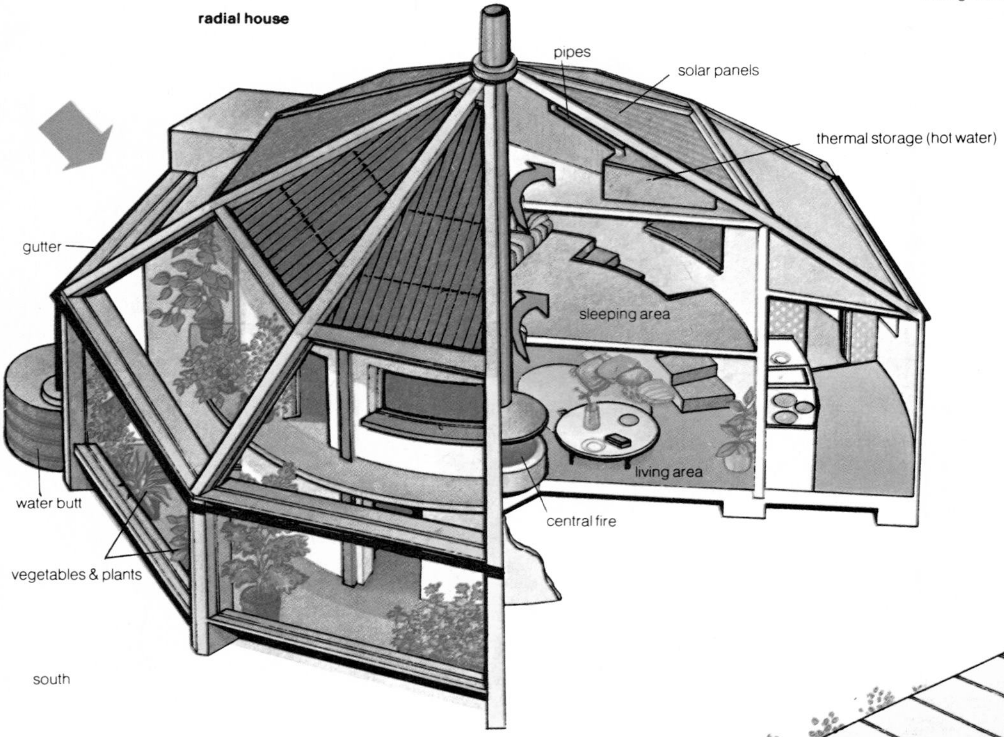

solar water heater

solar energy in

absorbers

energy transfer loop

electric booster

thermosyphon flow

storage tank

cold water in

hot water out

radial house

pipes

solar panels

thermal storage (hot water)

gutter

sleeping area

water butt

living area

central fire

vegetables & plants

south

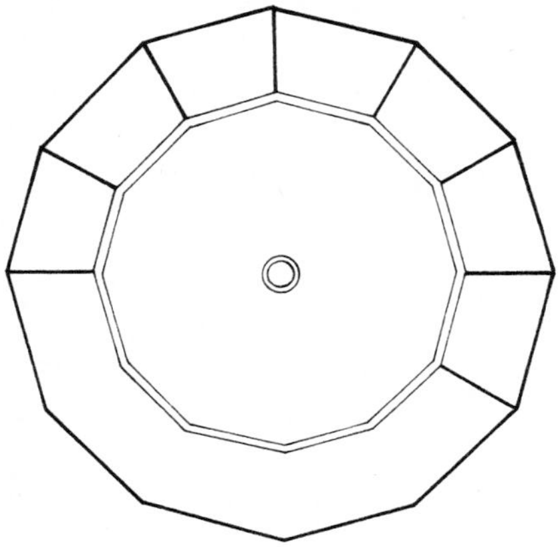

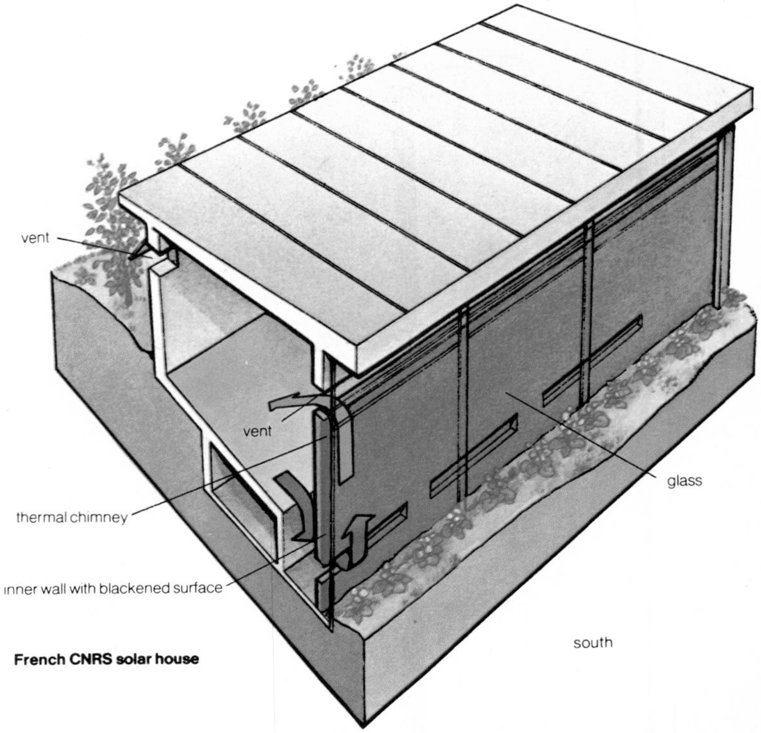

vent

vent

glass

thermal chimney

inner wall with blackened surface

south

French CNRS solar house

Top: the house of the future? As fossil fuel supplies dwindle, houses may rely more and more on solar energy for space and water heating. This American house has a solar roof for water heating.

Above: apparatus like this is a common sight in Israel. Water passed through the inclined panels is heated and is stored in the tank as the house's hot water supply. An electric booster may be necessary.

Left: various ways in which solar energy can be used for domestic heating systems. The radial house, designed by Herbert Girardet. This projected 'soft technology' house designed to be integrated in new, agriculturally based, village communities, uses solar energy both in the heating panels on the roof and in the greenhouse section for growing crops. The French CNRS solar house design has an outer south wall of glass and a blackened inner wall which is warmed by the sunlight. The thermal chimney which is created between the wall and the glass can be made to heat or cool the house as wished by opening and closing the vents as shown.

light, but they do not appreciably absorb longer wavelength infra-red radiation. Consequently they do not emit the latter wavelengths either and so cannot radiate heat, and therefore a spectrally selective *superblack body* reaches a higher temperature in sunlight than does a normal uniformly black body. Solar water heaters incorporating an absorbing surface of superblack anodized galvanized steel are commercially available. They absorb 93% of visible light but emit only 10% of their infra-red, and this produces an improvement in average performance of several per cent.

Solar houses Part of the heating and cooling requirements of a building can be provided by the solar energy falling on the roof or walls. Many designs have been proposed, and there are several hundred experimental solar buildings in existence, most of them in the United States, where the study of solar applications has been much advanced by the passing of the Solar Heating and Cooling Demonstration Act in September 1974. This Act provided, among other things, $60 million (£26 million) over five years for the design and erection of solar heated and cooled buildings, of all sizes from small family houses to large commercial buildings.

Solar heating occurs to some extent in all buildings, owing to sunlight warming the material or passing to the inside through windows. All well insulated buildings carefully designed to have a natural balance at a comfortable temperature are really in part solar heated, though they are not commonly thought of as solar buildings. There is a solar heated annexe of this type in St. George's School, Wallasey, Cheshire, in the U.K. This building has a south-facing glass wall combined with unusually high standards of insulation in the other three walls. It is heated almost entirely by solar energy, with some contribution from the heat generated by the lighting system and the occupants. Problems with ensuring an adequate supply of fresh air without losing too much heat have not, however, been solved.

The *Centre National de la Recherche Scientifique* of France has developed an interesting solar-driven air conditioning system which can provide warm or cool air for buildings as required. Thirty-six houses incorporating the CNRS system have been built in the South of France with funding from the French government to evaluate the design. Each house has a black-painted south-facing wall, capable of absorbing a great deal of heat, with an outer glass wall. Solar radiation is transmitted through the glass and warms this wall, creating a rising column of warmed air between the wall and glass. By adjustment of vents, the warmed air can be circulated to the interior of the house to heat it, or fresh cool air can be drawn through the building in summer. As the wall retains heat for several hours, the system continues to work after dark and during overcast portions of the day.

It is also possible to use solar water heaters to provide space heating and cooling in a building. Larger areas of collectors than needed simply to provide hot water are required, and the solar warmed water is stored in large tanks for circulation in the central heating system. In climates where summertime cooling is required, and night skies are generally clear, the same collectors can be used to chill the water very effectively during the night by pumping it through the collectors, which radiate heat to the sky. The chilled water can then, through an appropriate heat exchange system, be used to cool the house the next day.

A similar system, which uses a shallow reservoir of water on the roof of the building, has been developed in California. When winter heating is required, the reservoir is covered during the day by a black sheet which absorbs solar energy and warms the water beneath. Thermal insulation is rolled over this at night to prevent upward heat loss to the sky, so that the warm water warms the house beneath. During the summer, this insulation, which is white, is placed over the pond during the day to prevent the water from being warmed by the sun, but it is rolled back at night and the water is chilled by radiation loss and evaporation, and the house is subsequently cooled as interior heat is transferred to the cool reservoir.

In all such buildings, the initial costs tend to be rather higher than those of conventional buildings, and this is offset only by several years of fuel savings. As fuel prices rise, however, the economics of solar conditioned buildings are becoming steadily more attractive.

Other thermal uses
Solar distillation of brackish or saline water (DESALINATION) is carried out quite successfully on a small or medium scale in several countries, and some solar water or air heaters are in use in Australia and Russia for crop drying and timber curing. To obtain higher temperatures, it is necessary to focus sunlight by means of lenses or curved mirrors. Only direct sunlight, not diffuse daylight, can be focused in this way. In consistently sunny parts of the world, there is some interest in the use of focused collectors to boil water to raise steam. The steam could then be used to generate electricity by conventional means, or to provide mechanical power for applications such as pumping irrigation water.

Making electricity
The necessity for continuous electric power generation on space SATELLITES led to the development of the solar cell in the Bell Telephone Laboratories, USA, in the 1950s. These devices, which are generally made from thin slices of highly pure single crystal silicon, produce electric power from radiant energy. Wavelengths in the range 400–1100 nm (nanometres) are the most effective, and about half the solar spectrum falls in this range. The actual conversion efficiency of silicon cells is, however, considerably less than 50%, owing to various internal losses. The best cells available today convert sunlight to electric power with an efficiency of about 18% (the remainder of the energy is degraded to heat in the cell).

These cells contain added *dopants* (usually boron and arsenic) in small amounts to create in the crystal slice a junction between an *n*-type and a *p*-type SEMICONDUCTOR region. This creates a gradient of electric potential within the crystal, and when light falls on the crystal and excites electrons in it, creating electron-hole pairs, the junction separates the electrons and the holes, and a DC current flows. These cells have no storage capacity, and for terrestrial applications they are used in conjunction with electrical storage batteries. They are at present much too expensive for widespread use on Earth, though new manufacturing methods being developed in the United States may greatly reduce their cost.

Even if the cost were low, one disadvantage would still be the low efficiency. To operate a 500 W electric fire would require 2½ square metres (12 square feet) of cells even with maximum sunlight shining directly on them. Unless a large scale method of ENERGY STORAGE or transmission of electricity is employed, this power would have to be used fairly close to its source of production, where it is probably not needed anyway. One possible solution to this problem in the future may be to equip a satellite with large arrays of solar panels generating power which would be transmitted to Earth by means of MICROWAVES. These could be picked up by receiving stations consisting of arrays of wires even on cloudy days at fairly high latitudes, where the energy is required.

JAMES BLAKE

SOLDERING
Soldering refers to a technique for joining two or more pieces of metal with a metallic bonding alloy (*solder*). *Soft* soldering, the most common form, requires a temperature of at least 180°C (356°F). (BRAZING and WELDING are similar techniques which require much higher temperatures but produce much stronger joints.) The solder itself is a metal alloy with a melting point lower than that of the parent metals to be joined. It is heated and introduced to the metals at the joint, where a chemical process called *wetting* takes place. The hot solder forms a thin film between the surfaces of the two metals to be joined, and, as the metals partially melt, a new alloy is formed at the joint. The joint is thus composed of two layers of the new alloy (solder plus parent metal) and a thin layer of solder between them.

Solder The composition of solder varies according to the purpose for which it is intended. The most common soft solder is an alloy of 60% tin and 40% lead, and is used to make electrical connections. Hard solders are usually alloys containing silver, copper, zinc or aluminium. (The tin content of soft solders can be increased when the parent metals have relatively high melting points; brazing is done when the parent metals have especially high melting points or where joints capable of bearing considerable stress are needed.) Metals such as aluminium, which do not readily form alloys, require solder containing a high proportion of the parent metal. The solder used to join two bars of aluminium, for example, should contain a good deal of aluminium to facilitate the formation of a bonding alloy at the joint.

Soldering methods Because most metals that are exposed to the air form oxides, the surface to be joined must be de-oxidized so that the solder can readily form an alloy. Any reducing action is further complicated by the tendency of

Above left: soldering electrical connections. The solder is melted against the hot iron and makes a contact which is easy to undo if repairs are needed.

Above: a 'gadroon mount' being soldered to the body of a teapot. The solder is run around the seam using an oxy-acetylene flame.

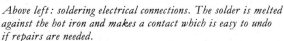

Above right: mass-production soldering. The electronic components, with connections underneath, are passed over trays of hot solder. Note the bank of blocks of solder in the rack above.

metals to oxidize when they are subjected to heat. To overcome these problems, acidic fluxes are used. The flux, which melts at a lower temperature than the solder, cleans the oxide surface barrier away and coats the parent metal so that further oxidation does not occur.

Any hot piece of metal can serve as a soldering iron. (For brazing and welding, gas flames are used.) Since soldering is used most often for joining electrical components, where changes in the resistance to the passage of an electric current can cause serious local heating problems, the less solder used to make a joint the better. Thus soldering irons, measured in wattage and having a copper bit, are usually more effective for precise operations. The wattage of the iron must be suitable for a particular job, and the size and shape of the bit is determined by the size of the joint to be made. The bit, which is sometimes plated with tin to prevent oxidation, must heat sufficiently to melt the solder and to compensate for heat lost to the parent metals. The typical job, soldering electrical components, using a 60% tin and 40% lead solder, requires a tip heated to 220°C (428°F) for the solder to melt (MP of the solder is 183°C; 361°F). With electrical components, too, there is a danger of the bit damaging sensitive parts, so irons have been developed with

devices to ensure an exact source of heat. To prevent the flux from burning off, for example, magnetically controlled bits are used. These bits are based on the principle of the specific *Curie point*, that temperature at which a piece of magnetic metal loses its magnetism. A small piece of metallic material is embedded in the bit; when it reaches a certain temperature, the loss of magnetism causes it to move and operate a switch to prevent further heating until the temperature has dropped to just below its specific Curie point.

The great advantage of soldered joints is their impermanence: if an electrical component needs to be replaced, the solder which holds it can be removed as easily as it was applied. Industrial soldering is based on the principle of mass production, and very few individual joints are soldered by hand. A piece of equipment can be assembled and then passed on an assembly line over a trough of molten solder so that the suspended components are automatically joined. Alternatively, preformed bits of cold solder can be fitted around electrical components and then melted into the parent metal with local resistance heating.

Soldering came into its own as a technique for making joints between pieces of metal when modern electrical technology necessitated tiny, impermanent links between separate components. But despite its usefulness in the past, and despite modern industrial processes such as dip soldering, wave soldering and even gas lamps to melt the solder and flux (now usually contained in the solder) solder is rapidly being replaced by more effective wrap-joints. Wrap-joints are square or oblong metal pegs which form convenient joints as wire can be wrapped by powerful tools into them. The wire is actually made to cut into the peg at a controlled torque, so that the joint is safe from gas corrosion. Hundreds of joints can be wrapped at the same time by assembly line machinery, and they can be dis-assembled just as quickly.

SOLENOID

A solenoid is an electrical device consisting simply of a coil of wire, and can be made, for example, by wrapping wire around a cylinder. When a current passes through the wire a magnetic field is set up (see ELECTROMAGNETISM), and this is made to move a ferrous core to actuate valves, switches and other devices. The solenoid is therefore a direct application of an electromagnet.

Outside the solenoid the lines of magnetic flux behave in a similar fashion to those of a bar magnet. A solenoid freely suspended horizontally in the Earth's magnetic field will set itself along a North-South line. Its ends behave like the poles of a bar magnet (see MAGNETISM), their polarity depending on the direction of the current in the spiral. Any ferrous material brought into the vicinity of the solenoid will be attracted to the poles along the lines of the magnetic field.

The strength of the magnetic field within the solenoid is uniform for most of its length but near the ends, known as the poles, the field diverges. At the poles the field strength dies rapidly to about one half of the strength in the centre. Inside the solenoid, at distances from one end of greater than about $3\frac{1}{2}$ times the diameter of the coil cross section, the field strength is 99% of the calculated value for an infinitely long solenoid. Hence in practice a 'long' solenoid should have a length at least seven times its diameter.

Applications The ability of the solenoid to produce a magnetizing force leads to its use in starting devices and power operated valves, as only a switch need be turned to energize it. For example, solenoid switches are widely used to engage starter motors in cars. Here two solenoids, the 'draw-in' coil and the 'holding' coil, are mounted on top of the starter motor with a plunger running through the inside of both (thus operating in the region where the field strength is uniform and at a maximum). One end of the plunger is attached to a lever which engages and disengages the starter motor pinion with the flywheel. The other end of the plunger is connected to a switch.

When the ignition switch is turned, the 'draw-in' coil is energized and the plunger is drawn to the right, thus engaging the starter motor with the flywheel. When the plunger makes contact with the switch the 'holding' coil and the starter motor are energized and the 'draw-in' coil is short circuited. This is because the 'draw-in' coil drains more power from the battery than is needed to just hold the plunger in position, and this power is now required to turn the starter motor. After the engine has started, the ignition switch is released, the 'holding' coil is de-energized and a spring returns the plunger to its original position, thus disengaging the starter motor from the flywheel.

In a simple power operated switch, such as one would find in a domestic central heating system, the solenoid provides the power to open and close the valve disc. The disc is connected by a rod to the core of the solenoid. When the solenoid is de-energized, the disc is held against the aperture by a spring and the valve is off. Switching on a current through the solenoid produces a magnetic field which draws the rod, and therefore the valve disc, away from the aperture, so that the valve is on. When the current is turned off the spring returns the disc, thus shutting the aperture and the valve.

SOLID (see matter, properties of)
SOLID STATE (see semi-conductors)
SONAR (see asdic & sonar)

Above: solenoid operated rotary switch with multiple contacts. Electromagnet switches contacts with ratchet mechanism.

Right: two applications of a solenoid. The starter motor arrangement for an internal combustion engine can be operated by two solenoids— one draws in the clutch and the other holds this position while the motor turns the engine. Solenoid valves are used extensively in industry for control purposes.

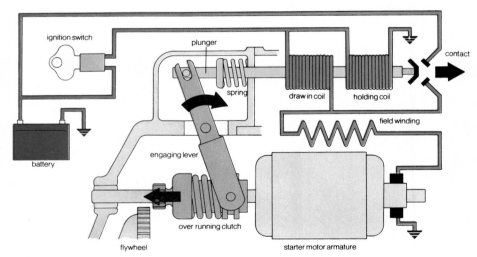

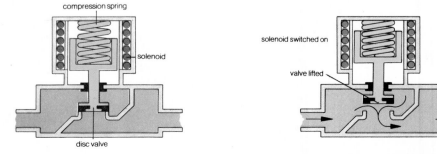

SORPTION

Words in common use such as 'absorb' and 'absorbent' describe the process of soaking up (from the Latin word *sorbere*), for example when porous materials soak up a spilled liquid. The term ADsorption was introduced to describe the attachment of gases to a surface. Thus a distinction is made with gas ABsorption, where the molecules of the gas would actually penetrate into the bulk of an absorbing solid (or liquid). The general term *sorption* includes both phenomena, adsorption and absorption, because they may occur simultaneously or be difficult to distinguish. Sorption phenomena are remarkable both for their complexity and for the many useful applications in which they are involved. Applications involving gases or vapours include air pollution control, drying processes and solvent recovery. Adsorption from liquids on to solid surfaces is the essential phenomenon which makes it possible to use porous solids to purify or decolorize food, beverages and domestic water supplies. The action of many CATALYSTS is closely connected with sorption phenomena.

Adsorption

When studying the adsorption of a gas on a solid surface, two types are recognized, namely *physical adsorption* and *chemical adsorption*, usually abbreviated to *chemisorption*. In physical adsorption the forces which bind the molecules to the surface, called *van der Waals forces*, are relatively weak and the phenomenon is akin to condensation; the most easily liquefiable gases or vapours are the most readily adsorbed. Physical adsorption is very rapid and the process is reversible, that is, the adsorbed gas can be pumped off the surface without having suffered chemical change. The surface area of adsorbents and catalysts can be found by measuring the amount of gas physically adsorbed.

RONAN PICTURE LIBRARY

Above: an illustration dating from about 1850 showing fuller's earth (a type of clay) being used to remove grease from textiles. After treatment with fuller's earth, the cloth was placed in troughs behind fulling stocks and then pounded with square-ended mallets. The grease is adsorbed on to the fuller's earth particles.

Below: gas masks of this type were developed in World War 2 for people suffering from respiratory complaints. One of the main filter materials was charcoal, a good absorbent material for poison gases.

RADIO TIMES HULTON PICTURE LIBRARY

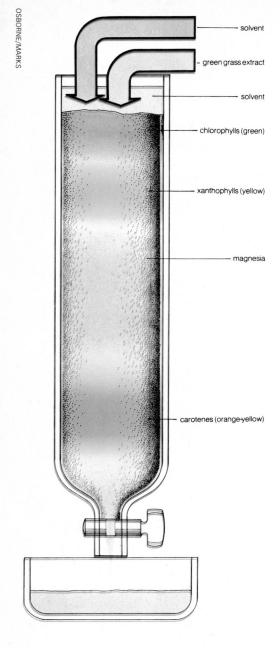

solvent

green grass extract

solvent

chlorophylls (green)

xanthophylls (yellow)

magnesia

carotenes (orange-yellow)

In chemisorption, the adsorbed molecules are held by stronger forces, similar to those involved in chemical combination. The rate of chemisorption may be increased by raising the temperature. Chemisorption is often irreversible, that is the adsorbed molecules are difficult to remove from the surface and may have undergone chemical change. In a chemical reaction which is being accelerated by the presence of a solid catalyst, an essential step is the chemisorption of one or more of the reactants on to the catalyst surface. Knowledge of the state of molecules chemisorbed on surfaces has expanded greatly in recent years as new instrumental techniques have been developed, for example *LEED* (low energy electron diffraction) or older techniques adapted, for example infra-red SPECTROSCOPY.

Absorption When a substance has been adsorbed on to the surface of a solid or liquid, it may further penetrate below the surface and become absorbed, either dissolving in the solid or liquid or reacting subsequently to form a chemical compound. Palladium (see PLATINUM METALS) is remarkable among metals in its ability to absorb large quantities of hydrogen, expanding about 10% in volume as the ratio of absorbed hydrogen atoms to palladium atoms attains a value of 0.6. Permeation of hydrogen through the walls of palladium tubes is a method for obtaining extremely pure hydrogen, because impurity molecules are held back. Gas-liquid absorption processes are often used in the chemical industry; process gas streams are intimately contacted with a suitable liquid so that a reaction is initiated, a pollutant removed, or a product recovered.

Sorbent materials *Activated carbons* may have a surface area of 1000 square metres per gramme (7·0 acres per ounce); it is this enormous area which makes them effective adsorbents. A network of fine pores penetrates throughout each carbon particle and the walls of these pores provide a vast *internal surface*. To make activated carbon, naturally occurring materials such as peat, wood, or coconut shell are first carbonized and then the pore system is developed by reaction with steam at 900 to 1000°C (1650 to 1830°F). Sorbent materials are classified according to their pore diameter: *macropores* have diameters above 200 angstroms, *transitional pores* have diameters of from 20 to 200 angstroms and *micropores* have diameters below 20 angstroms (one angstrom is equal to one ten millionth of a millimetre). By choice of raw material and activating treatment, carbons with a wide variation of adsorptive properties can be prepared to suit different applications. Activated carbons are widely used to adsorb impurities from the air or water supplies and to decolorize solutions of sugar during refining.

Silica gel is a hard glassy substance used as a drying agent (the term 'gel' merely indicates its condition at one stage of manufacture). Because of its highly porous nature it can adsorb as much as 40% of its own weight of water vapour. Other solid sorbents, for example calcium chloride, which is used as a laboratory *desiccant* (drying agent), remove water by forming chemical compounds, and may be discarded after use.

The ability to act as *molecular sieves*, which sort mixtures of molecules according to their size and shape, is the remarkable property of mineral and synthetic *zeolites*. About 50 years ago it was discovered that partially dehydrated *chabasite* (an alumino-silicate) would adsorb small molecules but not larger ones and

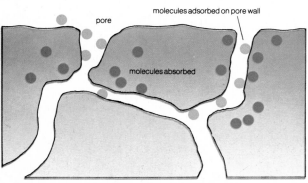

pore

molecules adsorbed on pore wall

molecules absorbed

Far left: grass extract is placed at the top of a column of magnesia powder which adsorbs the component dyes differently so they separate from one another when solvent is run through the column. The diagram below shows the difference between adsorption and absorption.

it was deduced that the pores must be less than five angstroms in diameter. These pores are, in reality, regularly arranged cavities which arise as a consequence of the way in which the atoms in its crystal lattice are arranged. Gas molecules enter through the usual pore system, but the smaller ones can then pass through 'windows' into the cavities where they are trapped.

Hard water containing calcium and magnesium IONS causes scale in kettles and water pipes, and a grey scum is precipitated when washing with soap. *Ion-exchange resins* are used in water softening (see WATER SUPPLY) because at ion-active sites on the surface, 'hard' calcium and magnesium ions are taken out of the water and 'soft' sodium ions are substituted. When the

Below: silica gel in a PVC cover protects an aircraft from moisture.

Below centre: an installation for drying and purifying carbon dioxide has columns filled with activated alumina adsorbent material.

Bottom: a column containing silica gel (right) is used to dry gases in a modern biological laboratory.

water softening capacity of the resin has been exhausted, it is regenerated with a strong solution of common salt (sodium chloride) which recharges the surface of the resin with sodium ions.

In chemistry and biology, it is often necessary to separate the components of a mixture, and use is made of the fact that some will adsorb strongly, and some weakly, on an appropriate solid adsorbent. In 1906, the Russian biologist Tswett applied a solution of plant pigments to the top of a glass tube packed with finely powdered chalk and washed it down with light petroleum. A series of horizontal coloured bands began to separate, including the green chlorophyll band. Pigments which were least strongly adsorbed on the chalk moved rapidly down the column, whereas the more strongly adsorbed pigments were held back. Other forms of CHROMATOGRAPHY (literally 'colour writing') were subsequently developed and are widely used for the separation and analysis of gases and liquids.

A large surface area is usually an essential requirement for an active catalyst, because one or more of the chemical reactants are chemisorbed on the catalyst surface. Some catalytically active substances cannot be prepared with a stable high surface area, or else they are so expensive (platinum for example) that maximum use must be made of small amounts. The solution to both these problems is to disperse the active catalytic material over the large surface of a porous solid such as alumina, silica gel or charcoal.

SOSIGENES of Alexandria (1st cent BC)

Sosigenes of Alexandria was an astronomer and mathematician who was employed by Julius Caesar to devise a more accurate calendar, which became known as the Julian calendar. He is not to be confused with Sosigenes the Peripatetic (2nd century AD), who was a Greek philosopher.

The old Roman Republican calendar had 355 days in the year (roughly 12 lunar months). It had once had 10 months, but very soon January and February were added to the beginning—this is why, for example, October (Latin *octo*, eight) is the tenth month. Every two years, 27 or 28 days were *intercalated*—added to the year after 23 February, the remaining five days of that month being dropped. This gave an average of $366\frac{1}{4}$ days, more than a day longer than the true solar year. As a result, by 47 BC the year was four months out of phase with the seasons. The problem was how to have the months in line with the phases of the moon, while at the same time keeping the year even with the seasons.

At the suggestion of Sosigenes, the old lunar calendar was abandoned altogether, the months were arranged on a seasonal basis, and a *tropical* (solar) year was adopted, similar to that of the Egyptian calendar but with $365\frac{1}{4}$ days instead of 365. To repair the discrepancy between the calendar date and the equinox, two intercalations were made in the year 46 BC: the one due that year of 23 days, and an insertion of two months between November and December, making 90 days in all for the year. There was to be an extra day every four years to keep the average at $365\frac{1}{4}$.

Unfortunately, the Romans practised inclusive numbering, which meant that they counted each leap year as the first in the next four-year period. As a result, in the next 36 years 12 days instead of nine were added. The Roman Emperor Augustus made a correction by eliminating the extra days between 8 BC and 4 AD, so that it took a total of 48 years for the Romans to get their calendar straightened out.

Above: this unusual calendar was found in Alaska, which belonged to Russia until 1867. It shows the saints' days of the Orthodox Church, which still uses Sosigenes' Julian calendar.

Not much is known about Sosigenes himself. His writings are all lost, except for fragments. The most interesting fragment which survives mentions his belief that Mercury revolves around the Sun, more than 1500 years before COPERNICUS demonstrated the plausibility of a Sun-centered system.

Further corrections to the calendar were made. February in the Julian calendar originally had 29 days, but in 44 BC the Roman Senate re-named the month of Quintilis, calling it July in honour of Julius Caesar, and in 8 BC Augustus re-named the month of Sextilis after himself. He increased it to 31 days, taking a day away from February, so that his month would have as many days as Julius'. More importantly, the solar year has 365.242199 days in it, rather than exactly 365.25; in October 1582 a Papal Bull of Pope George XIII corrected the calendar by 10 days, and decreed that henceforth centennial years would not be leap years unless divisible by four. For this reason, 1700, 1800 and 1900 were not leap years, but the year 2000 will be a leap year.

The new calendar is known as the Gregorian calendar. For various political and religious reasons it was not immediately adopted everywhere; in 1752, when it was adopted in Britain, legislation was carefully drafted to avoid various injustices, but there were still riots, because the people thought they were being cheated out of eleven days (not ten, because 1700 had been a leap year under the Julian system). The Gregorian calendar has still not been accepted by the Russian Orthdox Church; after the Revolution of 1917, however, the new Soviet government adopted the new calendar. Books about Russian history often give dates of events before 1917 in both 'old style' and 'new style'.

From the early Roman to the Julian calendar

Introduced:	c 753 BC ?Romulus		c 650 BC Numa Pompilius		47 BC Julius Caesar	
Average length of year:	304 days		355 (366.25*)		365 (365.25†)	
Months:			Januarius	(29)	Januarius	(31)
			Februarius	(28)	Februarius	(29†§)
Actual length of tropical year: 365.242199 days	Martius	(31)	Martius	(31)	Martius	(31)
	Aprilis	(30)	Aprilis	(29)	Aprilis	(30)
	Maius	(31)	Maius	(31)	Maius	(31)
	Junius	(30)	Junius	(29)	Junius	(30)
Actual length of lunar month: 29.530598 days	Quin(c)tilis	(31)	Quintilis	(31)	Quintilis‡	(31)
	Sextilis	(30)	Sextilis	(29)	Sextilis§	(30§)
	September	(30)	September	(29)	September	(30)
	October	(31)	October	(31)	October	(31)
Actual number lunar months per year: 12.368267 i.e. about 12 months and 11 days	November	(30)	November	(29)	November	(30)
	December	(30)	December	(29)	December	(31)
Average length of Gregorian (modern) year: 365.2425 days	Since this year was completely different from the solar year, it was probably allowed to 'drift' through the seasons.		* A 27- or 28-day intercalary month was inserted after 23 February every other year and the last 5 days of February were omitted. Occasionally the intercalary month was not inserted.		† An extra day was added to February every 4th year. ‡ Quintilis later called Julius. § Sextilis later called Augustus, increased to 31 days; Februarius reduced to 28.	

SOUND

Sound travels from its source to the observer in the form of waves. The essential requirement for the generation of such waves is the presence of a material medium containing particles able to interact with each other. This requirement is satisfied by the presence of a gas, liquid or a solid but, unlike ELECTRO-MAGNETIC waves, sound waves cannot be transmitted through a vacuum.

The study of such waves is termed *acoustics* and, strictly speaking, sound concerns those acoustic waves that are detectable by the human ear. The ear cannot detect acoustic waves having frequencies of vibration below 20 cycles per second (these are termed *infrasonic*) or above 20,000 cycles per second (ULTRASONIC).

Production and transmission of sound

When an object vibrates in air, the air molecules next to its surface are alternately pushed together and pulled apart—compressed and rarefied. As these molecules move back and forth they collide with neighbouring molecules, which are therefore also compressed and rarefied. A series of compressions and rarefactions is thus transmitted.

If the rate at which these transmitted vibrations occur is within a certain range (the *audible range*), the alternating vibrations of the air adjacent to the eardrum cause it to vibrate in sympathy. These vibrations are then transmitted through the ear to the brain, where they are interpreted as sounds.

If the material between the vibrating object and the ear or detector is a liquid or a solid, the sound is transmitted in a slightly different manner. In solids and liquids the molecules are held together by forces, the magnitude of which depends on the elastic properties of the material. The velocity of any compression wave depends upon the rate with which the displaced particles in its path return towards their undisturbed position. This rate of return is determined by the restoring influence acting on the particle and this increases with the modulus of ELASTICITY of the medium. Thus, the velocity of sound in a medium increases with increasing modulus of elasticity—that is, as the medium becomes less elastic. Also, the rate of return of particles to the equilibrium position (and, therefore, the velocity of sound) is retarded or inhibited by the inertia of the medium, that is, by interference effects between the molecules within the medium. This is effectively represented by the *density* of the material. It can be shown that, for a sound wave travelling through any medium, the velocity at which it travels is given by the square root of the ratio of the modulus of elasticity to density.

In general, sound waves travel faster through both solids and liquids than they do through gases, owing to the extra time required for collisions to occur between the molecules of a gas (gases are more elastic, and so have a lower modulus of elasticity). But since solids are less elastic than liquids, sound waves travel faster through solids than through liquids. The velocity of sound in steel is approximately 5000 metres per second (5000 m/s; 11,180 mph); in water approximately 1400 m/s (3130 mph); and in air at room temperature and at sea level the velocity of sound is 344 m/s (769 mph).

The main determining factors effecting the velocity, namely elasticity and density, do not change regularly with temperature in solids and liquids, and temperature changes thus have little effect on the velocity of sound in such materials. In the case of gases, however, temperature changes have a pronounced effect on velocity, since increasing the temperature causes the gas molecules to move from collision to collision with greater speed. The velocity of sound in air for example increases from 331 m/s (741 mph) at 0°C to 386 m/s (864 mph) at 100°C.

Properties of sound waves

Audible sounds are characterized and compared in terms of pitch, loudness and quality. The pitch of a note is the frequency of the sound producing it, and is thus analogous to the colour of visible LIGHT. The loudness of a sound is a subjective sensation dependent on the listener, but is a function of the *energy* of the transmitted sound wave (see NOISE MEASUREMENT). The quality of a note is that characteristic of the emitted sound that enables a listener to distinguish between a note played on a piano and a note of the same frequency and loudness played on the violin. Quality is often termed the *timbre* of the note, and is governed by the shape of the wave profile of the sound.

Sound waves exhibit properties common to other forms of wave motions, for example electromagnetic radiation, namely reflection, refraction, interference and diffraction.

Reflection

Sound waves are reflected from surfaces in their path in the same way as reflection occurs in OPTICS. It is the reflection of sound from solid surfaces that causes the production of echoes, and the Whispering Gallery at St Paul's Cathedral, London, behaves as it does because sound, reflected at grazing incidence from its walls, is confined close to the surface with very little loss of energy. This results in sounds of very low intensity emitted at one side of the gallery being audible at the other side.

Below: early demonstration of Chladni figures—patterns of sand on a vibrating plate. The sand collects at points of no vibration (nodes). Nodes are created by touching the plate with a finger.

Reflection of sound is of major importance in building design from an acoustic point of view. In a hall sounds are heard from different directions at different times. The sound arrives at the listener directly from the source, from echoes produced by the walls and ceilings and also after repeated and multiple reflections from the various surfaces within the hall. At each reflection some loss of energy occurs until eventually it diminishes to below the level at which the sound can be heard. The persistence of sound after emission is known as *reverberation*.

The sound quality observed by a listener depends on the time for which reverberation occurs. A very short reverberation time of the order of 0.5 seconds causes orchestral music to sound thin and lifeless, whereas an overlong period of reverberation causes music to sound muffled. The technical problems of acoustic design were first systematically investigated in America by W C Sabine in 1906.

He found that the reverberation time depended on the volume of the room, the surface area and the sound absorbing characteristics of the surfaces. Porous materials such as cork, polystyrene foam and soft furnishings are generally good absorbers of sound, while hard smooth surfaces such as glass and glazed tiles, and materials of high density such as brickwork, plaster and concrete, are poor absorbers.

By judicious choice of the shape of surfaces, construction materials and furnishings, the reverberation time and hence the acoustic properties of any room or auditorium may be predetermined at the design stage.

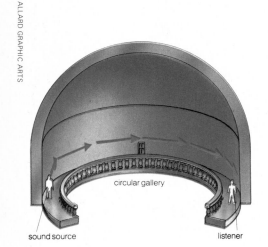

circular gallery

sound source

listener

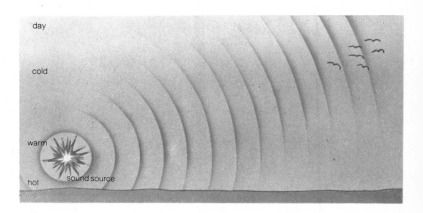

day

cold

warm

hot

sound source

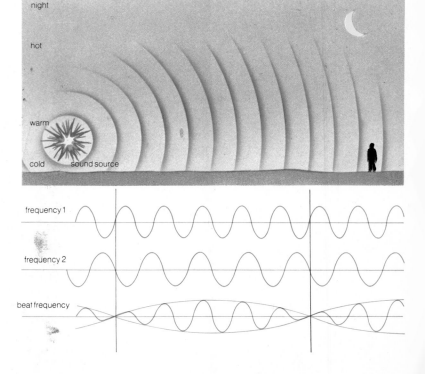

night

hot

warm

cold

sound source

frequency 1

frequency 2

beat frequency

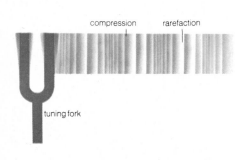

compression   rarefaction

tuning fork

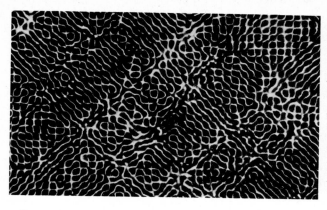

IBM/ALPHABET & IMAGE

For certain specialized purposes, such as the testing and design of LOUDSPEAKERS, it is necessary to construct rooms whose walls absorb completely all the sound energy falling on them. This is done by completely lining the room, called an *anechoic chamber*, with blocks of highly porous materials.

Refraction Sound waves are found to change direction when they pass into and through regions where a change of velocity occurs. Since the temperature of a gas affects the velocity at which sound travels through it, atmospheric temperature variations can result in velocity changes and consequent direction changes of the sound. This change of direction is called refraction and is directly comparable to refraction in optics.

This effect is the cause of sound carrying further and being easier to hear at night than during the daytime. By day, the upper layers of air are generally colder than those at ground level and sound waves are thus refracted away from the earth's surface. At night, the reverse situation is the usual one and the colder layers of air are those near the ground. This results in the sound being refracted back towards the Earth's surface and being heard over long distances and at enhanced intensity.

Interference Two sound waves of the same frequency interfere when they arrive at the same point after travelling

Above left: complicated Chladni figures in quartz sand on a square steel plate created by a forcing frequency of 15.2 kHz.
Above: hexagonal structure resulting from vibrating a liquid with the aid of a high frequency sound wave. The pattern on the surface—'frozen' with a stroboscope—is related to the liquid density and viscosity and the frequency and amplitude of the forcing vibration.

different distances.

If the waves arrive at that point in such a way that positions of maximum disturbance coincide, the waves reinforce each other, producing a loud sound. This is *constructive* interference. If a position of minimum disturbance coincides with a maximum, cancellation or *destructive* interference occurs and the sound is of a diminished intensity.

Interference of two sound waves is also apparent when they are of slightly different frequencies. This interference causes a phenomenon known as *beats* to occur. Beats are heard by the observer as bursts of increased intensity superimposed on a lower volume background. The number of beats heard in one second, the beat frequency, is equal to the difference in frequency between the two sounds producing them.

This effect is used to tune one string of a musical instrument with another. The two strings are sounded together, and the

Left: repeated reflections from the surfaces of a dome gives rise to the effect for which the Whispering Gallery at St Paul's Cathedral is renowned.
Refraction of sound due to temperature gradients causes sounds to travel further at night than during the day. A vibrating object, such as a tuning fork, sets up longitudinal waves consisting of a series of alternate compressions and rarefactions. Two waves of slightly different frequency interfere to give periodic rise and fall of volume known as beats. The frequency of the beats is the difference between the two initial frequencies.

Right: recording and rehearsal studio at the Sydney Opera House, Australia.

PHOTOGRAPHIC LIBRARY OF AUSTRALIA

tension of one of them (and hence the transmitted frequency) is varied so as to slow down the beat frequency until no beats are heard.

Diffraction All waves normally travel in straight lines, but they can bend around obstacles whose size approximately equals the wavelength of the radiation. Since the wavelengths of sound waves are normally between several inches and feet in length, they bend around most commonly encountered objects, whereas the short wavelengths of light means that it is not diffracted by ordinary objects. It is thus possible to hear sounds from sources that cannot be seen by the observer.

The Doppler effect When a source of sound and the listener are moving relative to each other, an apparent change in the pitch of the sound is observed.

An everyday example of this is the sound heard from the ground when a low flying jet aircraft passes overhead. The pitch of the sound seems to drop suddenly as it passes the observer. The actual frequency of the emitted sound remains constant but, while the aircraft approaches, more sound waves reach the observer in a given time than are emitted in that time, resulting in the increased frequency of sound received by the observer.

As the source passes, and the distance between the source and the observer increases, the number of waves reaching the observer in a given time becomes less than the number emitted in that time and the listener thus hears a sudden decrease in the pitch.

Infrasonic and ultrasonic vibrations Pressure waves having frequencies outside the normal range of detection of the human ear are termed *infrasonic* and *ultrasonic* vibrations. Vibrations with frequencies below 20 cycles per second are in the infrasonic range, while ultrasonics are vibrations with frequencies above 20,000 cycles per second.

Any vibrations causing slow variations in the pressure of air or of the elastic behaviour of any other wave transmitting material may be regarded as infrasonic in character. Vibrations of the Earth's crust due to earthquake tremors typically fall in this category.

The high frequency vibrations that typify the ultrasonic range are commonly generated by quartz crystal OSCILLATORS. If a quartz crystal, cut in a certain manner, is compressed or extended, it exhibits opposite electrical charges on opposite faces. The reverse effect is observed when the crystal is subjected to a voltage. This is known as the PIEZO-ELECTRIC effect. If an alternating electric potential is applied to a quartz crystal, the crystal expands and contracts at the same frequency as the applied potential.

The amplitude of this vibration becomes large when the frequency of the alternating potential coincides with the natural frequency of vibrations of the crystal due to the RESONANCE effect. The vibration of the crystal can be used as a source of compressional waves, whose frequency is dependent on the dimensions of the crystal, but is normally well above the range of detection of the human ear, and thus *ultrasonic*.

Applications of acoustic vibrations Apart from the obvious uses of speech and music, there are many technical uses of compressional waves. Compressional waves conveyed by the Earth's crust can be detected on seismographs to locate and classify geophysical movements or to give information about rock structures through which they travel (see SEISMO-LOGY). Prospecting for natural resources such as oil and natural gas relies heavily on the information obtained from the reflection of acoustic waves from rock formations (see OIL

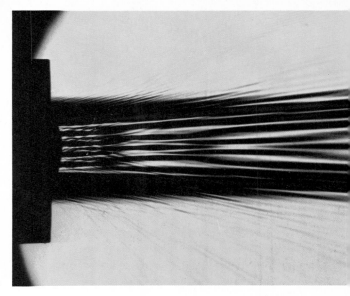

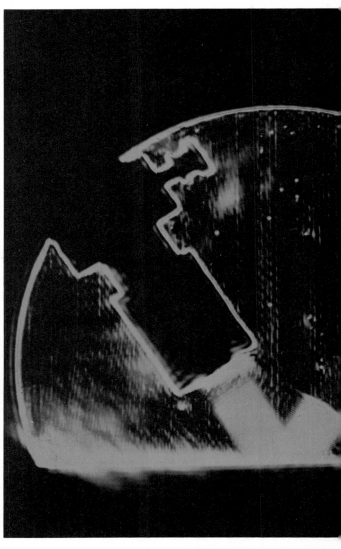

*Using a combination of optical
acoustics and schlieren techniques
it is possible to record sound
patterns, photographically.
Left: shows a diffraction pattern
produced by sound source left of
picture, obstructed by grating
consisting of 5 cylindrical
objects in a row. The high
intensity sound waves are blue.
Below left: a plane ultrasonic
beam (frequency 3 MHz)
viewed in laser light. The beam
is shown reflected from a
horizontal plate: the front of the
reflected sound pulse can be
clearly seen. Below: the complex
sound pattern produced by
reflecting the beam of sound
(produced at upper left) off the
structure; high intensities are red.*

EXPLORATION). Measurement of depth and location of hazard objects at sea also relies on the reflection of sonic waves (see ASDIC AND SONAR).

Ultrasonic vibrations have a wide range of applications. Important amongst these are ultrasonic cleaning, drilling and non-destructive testing of metal castings. When generated in liquids, ultrasonic waves produce *cavitation* by the creation of minute spaces within the liquid. This gives rise to a vacuum effect within the liquid which is extremely effective in removing dirt and dust particles from surfaces requiring cleaning. The effect is also used for emulsifying immiscible liquids (liquids which will not normally mix, like oil and water), and for the removal of air bubbles from liquids prior to casting.

Holes of any shape can be bored in a surface by the action of ultrasonic waves imposed on a rod in contact with the surface to be drilled. The cutting action is achieved with the aid of ABRASIVE powder, and the resulting hole is the shape of the vibrating rod. The principles of reflection of ultrasonic waves provides the basis for the detection of flaws, voids, cracks and other irregularities nondestructively in large metal castings (see QUALITY CONTROL).

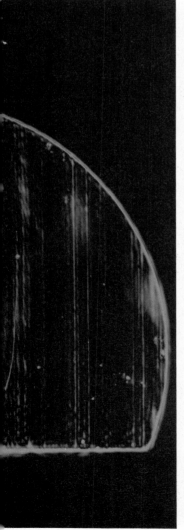

SOUND EFFECTS MACHINES

Sound effects used in the theatre, opera and broadcast drama fall into two categories: authentic sound, such as a gunshot, which is simply produced on cue, and simulated sound, produced by mechanical means. Since the perfection of recording techniques, especially MAGNETIC TAPE, a further distinction can be made between 'live' and recorded sound.

Sound in the theatre possesses qualities which may be altered during rehearsal by the director, including pitch, volume and duration. Recorded sound has obvious advantages with regard to volume, but may lack flexibility in pitch and duration. Furthermore, the recorded sound is governed by the circumstances of its recording and does not allow for adjustments during rehearsal. 'Live' sound, on the other hand, requires careful direction, but its advantages in timing and duration are manifold, especially where it accompanies action on the stage.

During the nineteenth century, opera and theatrical productions became quite elaborate, and there was a predilection for supernatural effects. Paradoxically, realism was demanded at the same time; this required ingenuity from both sound and scenic designers. Realism was often provided by the accommodation of authentic sounds; for example, the sound of horses' hooves was often provided by real horses, and blacksmiths hammered real anvils. Nowadays these sounds are usually recorded on tape, though often with a backup sound source. In the days before recorded sound, 'machines' were often built to provide simulated sounds, and many of these are still in use in today's theatres. For example, armies seldom march on boards, and it is a simple matter to build a shallow trough and fill it with gravel, so that three or four men can simulate the sound of boots trudging off to battle. Many sound effects 'machines' are a bit more elaborate.

Thunder   There are three categories of theatrical thunder; the thunderclap, the distant rumble, and a point between the two which is longer in duration than the 'clap' but just as sharp. The thunderclap machine consists of up to twenty wooden slats in pairs, hinged a few inches apart with a piece of rope. Another rope is fastened to the last slat in such a way that a sharp pull on it brings all the slats progressively but rapidly together. A distant rumble can be simulated by filling a cart with rubble such as bricks and large stones and mounting the cart on a set of uneven or eccentric wheels. The misshapen wheels cause the rubble to shift as the cart is pushed across the floor, emitting the desired continuous rumble. Finally, there is the thunder sheet, which is a thin, suspended piece of sheet metal which can be shaken with the required degree of violence. The duration of the sound of the rumble-cart and the thunder sheet is obviously easy to control, and the other qualities of these sounds are also controlled, for example by specifying the speed at which the cart is pushed.

Wind machine   This traditional machine has been elevated to the status of orchestral instrument in works such as Richard Strauss' tone poem *Don Quixote*. It consists of a slatted wooden drum mounted on a standing frame in such a way that it can be turned. Over the drum is draped a piece of canvas, fastened to the frame at one end and tied down or weighted at the other. The drum is turned by means of a handle and the scraping of the slats on the canvas produces the wind sound. Raising the pitch of the sound is accomplished by turning the drum faster.

Rainfall   A metal chute is constructed to form a zig-zag shape with varying depths and gradients. Dried peas or shot are poured into the top of the chute and in making its way through the gradients by force of gravity simulates the sound of falling rain.

Whip crack   This is another device that has been used in orchestral music. Two thin strips of wood about two feet (61 cm) long and about two inches (5 cm) wide are screwed to either side of a flat wooden handle. The construction is held by the handle in one hand and smacked against the palm of the other hand; the two long strips smacking together produce the required 'crack' of the whip. This device is also used to simulate the sound of a piece of wood breaking.

Railway sound   This is a wooden revolving drum similar to the wind machine, but with only two slats and having a metal covering. As the drum is rotated a roller-skate is pressed against it and as it passes the slats the wheels 'jump', producing the characteristic 'click-clack' of train wheels running over jointed rails.

Creaks, groans and squeaks   An open-ended barrel has a piece of three-ply wood fitted in one end, and a long, stout rope is passed through a hole in this new bottom. The rope is resin impregnated and, holding the rope taut, a piece of resinous leather is drawn along the rope near the open end of the barrel, which acts as a resonator. The machine can produce sounds from a squeak to a lion's roar, depending on the speed and abruptness of the action, and varying the resonance by reaching further into the barrel.

Aircraft engine   Leather strips are fitted to a shaft which is turned by an electric motor. The shaft is placed inside a wooden drum, and as it turns the leather strips beat against slats on the inside of the drum.

Left: the thunder barrel, behind the scenes at a mediaeval mystery play. The barrel contains pieces of rubble which tumble as they are turned, simulating the sound of thunder.

Below: BBC technicians at work. These photos were taken in the 1930s. The sound men listen to the programme being broadcast on headsets in order to produce the sounds on cue. The sounds of horses on gravel, an oar in water and rainfall are being simulated; one man carefully follows the script.

SOUNDPROOFING

Soundproofing is concerned with the exclusion of sounds from a particular location. This might be an open-plan office or classroom, a room in a home or a factory, or the interior of a motor vehicle.

When a problem in soundproofing arises, there are three factors to be considered. Firstly, the *source:* how much sound and from what direction. Secondly, the *path:* air-borne sound is called *noise,* but structure-borne sound, transmitted through walls, floors and so forth is called *vibration.* Thirdly, the effects of unwanted sound on a person—the *receiver* of sound—must be considered, in order to establish permissible levels.

Architecture   In the design of domestic and commercial buildings, provision is made to minimize the transmission of unwanted sound between rooms. One way to do this is to make floors and walls thick and heavy, but this is not always possible nowadays for economic reasons. Lighter panels have been developed which are quite rigid rather than heavy, thus providing some sound insulation. Some panels are coated with *viscoelastic* materials, such as rubber or vinyl, which further *damps* the sound. Sometimes an air space of a few inches is provided between two adjacent panels, giving further improvement by changing the material (solid to air to solid) through which the sound is travelling.

The same principles are used in windows for buildings. A single window pane of typical thickness (3 or 4 mm—$\frac{1}{8}$ or $\frac{1}{6}$ inch) will provide about 20 decibels (dB—see NOISE MEASUREMENT) of sound attenuation, reducing noise to about one-quarter loudness. If laminated glass is used, it will provide still more damping, and double glazing will cut the noise level by half as much again as a single pane. Sometimes the edges of the air space between two panes are lined with a soft fibrous material, which further reduces the problem by absorbing vibration.

Open-plan office space represents a real economic advantage, as well as design flexibility, and open-plan classrooms make possible new teaching methods, but when such architectural space was first designed, noise level proved to be a problem

Below: a Ford Granada undergoing noise tests in an anechoic chamber. Such a room absorbs sound, making possible testing under controlled circumstances.

because of the way sound will travel along walls which are not interrupted by partitions. Movable partitions are used to create acoustic environments, and soft, absorbent materials can be used in various places. Partitions and walls as well as floors can be covered with soft materials such as carpeting, felt, hessian and so forth. The height and absorptive treatment of the ceilings are of great importance in controlling the direction and loudness of intruding sound. Absorbent ceiling tiles are widely used in modern construction.

Factory noise

Industrial architecture is designed so that noisy areas will be insulated from noise sensitive areas by space which is not so sensitive, for example, storage or warehouse space. It is important in industrial soundproofing to insulate the sound source from the floor so that offending vibrations are damped; this is done by installing a relatively flexible element between two rigid structures. Springs, soft rubber mounts and cork are used to isolate a machine from the factory floor, effectively 'de-coupling' the machine from the structure. In addition, cavities inside machine housings or castings can be stuffed with absorbent materials such as foam rubber.

Motor vehicles

In cars, both noise and vibration control are necessary. At low speeds, airborne noise from the tyres can be a problem, while at higher speeds the noise due to air flow in window cracks and around the body of the car can be

Below : a cutaway model of a double glazing installation. The space between the panes or panels is lined on the sides with sound-absorbing materials ; double glazing reduces sound coming in from outside by a significant degree.

Below right : a sound proofing baffle with glass beads. This type of insulation is used in the exhaust system of a gas turbine driver in an industrial installation.

intrusive. During sudden acceleration, engine and exhaust system noise can be excessive.

Noise control in the design of motor vehicles amounts to a surprisingly costly item; many countries have legislation setting permissible noise levels in commercial vehicles, though no such protection exists for private cars. The aerodynamic design of a vehicle body is important, and manufacturers test scale models of new designs in wind tunnels partly for this reason. The SUSPENSION of a car is designed to isolate the body as much as possible from road shock. The engine is mounted on pads of rubber to damp vibration; large body panels may be attached to the car with rubber strips installed for the same purpose. The various parts of the car are designed so that one part will not be subject to *sympathetic vibration* with another; in other words, each part of the body shell should have a different *resonant frequency*. Rubber floormats, carpeting and upholstery inside the car are further considerations in decreasing interior noise. The undercoating of the car body, intended primarily to inhibit rust, also helps to damp unwanted sound.

Exterior noise from motor vehicles is increasingly regarded as a threat to the quality of life, especially in cities. Legislation requires proper maintenance of EXHAUST SYSTEMS, in particular silencers. In some cities the police are equipped with *sound level meters* for noise measurement.

Airport noise is another increasing problem which is impossible to solve to the satisfaction of those living in the neighbourhood, despite research into means of making the JET ENGINE quieter. Today the most common partial solution to the problem is the use of double glazing, but this, like the use of AIR CONDITIONING in commercial buildings so that doors and windows can be kept closed to keep out sound, is a stopgap measure. The increase of noise pollution in a modern industrial society will be of increasing concern in years to come.

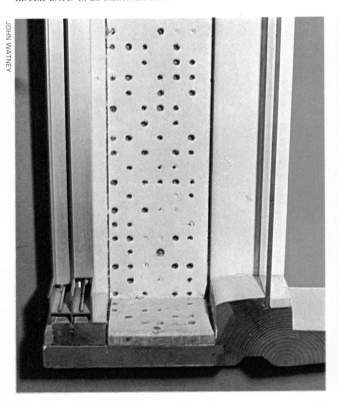

35 mm soundtracks, left to right: standard magnetic stripe without pictures, but including the balance stripe which is usually unrecorded though it could be used for special effects: some films even have a smell track, consisting of pulses which trigger odours released into the theatre; full magnetic base used in the editing stages; negative optical track; same track, positive and with pictures, as used in the projector.

SOUNDTRACK

In 1906 a Frenchman, Eugène Lauste, who had worked in Thomas Edison's laboratory, became interested in adding synchronized sound to the then very new motion pictures. Lauste's method was to photograph sound on to the actual picture negative. Inside the camera he fitted an exposure lamp and SOLENOID coil with a slit diaphragm, to which he connected a telephone microphone. Speech signals from the microphone vibrated the diaphragm assembly, which he called a *light valve*, causing variations in the intensity of light falling on to the film. Lauste also had to construct a special projector to reproduce this track, but since audio amplifiers had not yet been invented he was unable to reach a wide audience.

In 1922 an American scientist, Theodore Case, actually photographed sound waves by modulating an oxy-acetylene flame, but soon abandoned the commercial possibility, with his invention of a PHOTOELECTRIC CELL. He was able to demonstrate talking films in 1923, using a gas DISCHARGE TUBE for recording and his light sensitive photocell coupled to an Audion amplifier and loudspeaker. But film laboratories at that time were unable to give consistent results, and the surface noise for the film was extremely high.

The first motion pictures exhibited with synchronized soundtracks began to appear in 1927, such as *The Jazz Singer* starring Al Jolson. The sound for these early films was recorded either photographically on the film itself, or on a separate synchronized disc, so all film projectors had to be equipped for either system. The discs were 10 inches (40 cm) in diameter, played at a speed of $33\frac{1}{3}$ rpm, and contained a *start mark* on the inside groove—the end of the recording being the outside groove. There were 96 grooves to the inch, so that each disc lasted for 12 minutes, which was just sufficient to accompany 1000 feet (305 m) of picture film running at 24 frames per second. Since they were shellac pressings, these discs were extremely fragile and did not last more than a few years.

The early thirties showed a great improvement in laboratory control and film emulsions were manufactured particularly for sound on film recording. A system of background noise reduction was introduced in 1932, and most films today use photographic or *optical* soundtracks.

Optical sound

Cameras for producing optical soundtracks are available for 35 mm, 16 mm, and Super 8 mm film. The basic design consists of a light-tight film chamber, a film transport system with flywheel and sound drum, a detachable magazine for holding exposed and unexposed film, and an exposure lamp complete with optical system and modulator, to expose a track which varies in step with the sound vibrations. Two types of modulator are used, a *mirror* GALVANOMETER and a *light valve*. Both produce a *variable area* sound negative, in which a white band in the centre of a black strip changes its width. The galvanometer reflects light from the exposure lamp, via a V shaped mask, through a narrow horizontal slit. The light valve passes light directly through to the slit. In both cases an image of the slit is focused on to the film as it passes round the sound drum. A noise reduction *bias* is applied to the modulator when there is little or no sound, so that it passes the minimum amount of light, thus reducing unwanted background noise.

Negative exposure is accurately controlled, and development is carried out at a commercial laboratory on a continuous processing machine. The negative is developed to a specified density, which has been determined by previous tests with signals at two frequencies (usually 400 Hz and 6 kHz for 35 mm film). Since the negative is not suitable for reproduction, a print must be made before the soundtrack can be heard.

The optical soundtrack is printed on to the picture film in such a way that it is in advance of its corresponding picture frame by 20 frames on 35 mm, 26 frames on 16 mm, and 22 frames on Super 8 mm. This is because the film has to run through the projection gate jerkily, each frame of the film being motionless for a fraction of a second. The film must be running as smoothly as possible by the time the sound is picked up, so it is first passed round a series of loops, rollers and a *sound drum*. The sound drum is quite heavy so that its INERTIA smooths out any slight ripple which might occur.

The reproducer consists of an exciter lamp, slit and optical system, together with a light sensitive cell behind the film. The older type of photoelectric cell invented by De Forest has now been replaced by a photo-emissive cell, a *photo*DIODE, or an INTEGRATED CIRCUIT chip comprising a photodiode and amplifier. Soundtracks have an overall frequency response of 50 Hz to 8 kHz on 35 mm, 80 Hz to 6 kHz on 16 mm, and 100 Hz to 4 kHz on Super 8 mm. The frequency characteristic can be altered, and the signal-to-noise ratio improved, by the use of the *Dolby* noise reduction system (see TAPE RECORDER).

Magnetic sound

Magnetic recording began in 1898, when Valdemar POULSEN, a Danish engineer, gave a public exhibition of his *Telegraphone*. This instrument consisted of a piano wire 1.5 metres (59 inch) in length, along which was passed an electromagnet in close contact. The coil of the magnet was connected in series with a battery and carbon microphone from a telephone. The piano wire became magnetized by speaking into the microphone, and by substituting a telephone receiver the speech could be replayed. But it was 46 years later that Germany produced a tape recorder, the *Magnetophon*, to relay Hitler's messages to the army. After further development of the system in America, magnetic sound was introduced into the film industry during 1950. New techniques had to be learned for handling and synchronizing magnetic film, since recordings were invisible and unlike optical soundtracks to which everybody had become accustomed. The improvements obtained were virtually silent backgrounds, extended frequency response, immediate replay after recording, and quick methods of making copies.

All soundtracks nowadays originate on ¼ inch magnetic tape using portable recorders such as the *Nagra*, *Perfectone*, and *Stellavox*. In addition to the audio track, a separate *pulse track* is also recorded, which provides a speed reference of the picture camera. The selected material is transferred on to magnetic film for editing purposes, and the pulse track is used for synchronizing the tape to the magnetic film recorder. A wide magnetic stripe on clear 35 mm film base is preferred for editing, but fully coated magnetic film is used for recording up to 6 tracks on 35 mm film.

The component parts of a soundtrack, meaning dialogue, music, and effects, are synchronized to the edited picture and assembled into separate reels of magnetic film. There may be as many as 15 or 20 reels of sound for one reel of picture, and these are mixed together in a re-recording theatre equipped with a long sound MIXING console. Two or three balance engineers adjust volume levels and sound quality to the satisfaction of the producer, and a final three track magnetic master is recorded with dialogue on track 1, music on track 2, and effects on track 3. This allows for other languages to be substituted and mixed with the music and effects for different countries. The magnetic master is then re-recorded on to an optical sound negative for making standard release prints.

Some release prints have magnetic soundtracks, in which case a magnetic coating consisting of an iron oxide lacquer is applied to the film base after printing. 35 mm films have three magnetic stripes, or four stripes when small perforations are used. 70 mm films have six stripes, five of which feed loudspeakers behind the screen, and one feeds auditorium loudspeakers for 'surround sounds' and special effects (such as low-frequency earthquake sounds).

16 mm films may have perforations down both edges or just down one edge. In the former case, *edge* stripes have to be used —one thin stripe down each edge. In the latter, one edge of the film can be used for the soundtrack, which may be either all magnetic, all optical, or half and half—offering the possibility of dual language soundtracks. These are frequently used

Above: layouts of the soundtrack playing systems for both optical and magnetic tracks on a 16 mm projector. The edge of the film projects beyond the sound drum so that the light can shine through it; alternatively the magnetic head can be brought into use. On 16 mm both optical and magnetic heads come after the film gate.

on airline services offering in-flight movies. In all cases where stripe is added to the film after editing, a thin balance stripe must be added along the other edge so that the film will be the same thickness at both edges and will not wind up awkwardly on the spool.

Projectors for 35 mm and 70 mm films have penthouse sound heads—that is, they are between the upper spool box and the

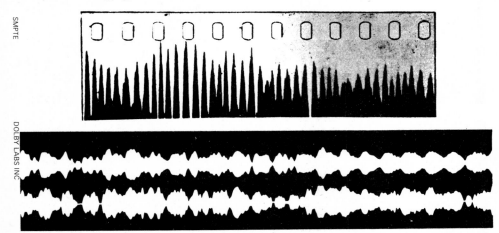

Left: the upper part is the soundtrack from one of Eugène Lauste's films made in 1910, basically the same system as used today. Not until improved electronics and loudspeakers came along could 'talkies' be a commercial success. Below it on a larger scale is the most recent development in stereo optical soundtracks using the Dolby noise reduction system, claimed to bring optical sound quality up to hi fi standards.

Right: machines such as these are used to make soundtracks.

picture gate, rather than below the gate. This gives a picture to sound separation of minus 24 frames for 70 mm and minus 28 frames for 35 mm. With 16 mm films the sound reproducer is below the picture gate, and the sync separation is 28 frames.

Other systems　New developments in soundtracks include a *hue-modulated* sound negative recorded on colour film. The system has signal peaks of red and green, and yellow for zero modulation. Experiments with *stereo optical* are being made with a twin-track Dolby encoded sound negative. A decoder is used for replay as three track stereo. *Quintophonic* consists of a three track magnetic stripe on 35 mm film with quadraphonic encoding (see STEREO). This can be replayed as five separate tracks. The *Imax* system uses 70 mm picture film projected horizontally, with separate six track magnetic sound replayed through 55 loudspeakers.

Amateur soundtracks　The first amateur sound films were recorded on 78 rpm discs coated with cellulose lacquer. These discs had the advantage of immediate replay, but were rather fragile and had a short life. Magnetic recording gave improved and permanent sound quality, and numerous mechanical and electrical devices were designed to synchronize a tape recorder to a projector. The various systems evolved meant that films were not interchangeable, and 'sync' was not always 100%.

The preferred method today is a magnetic stripe in liquid form, which is applied to the edited film. The soundtrack is recorded later on a projector, or sometimes during filming within the camera, with magnetic facilities, which gives good sound quality with a frequency range of 50 Hz to 8 kHz. Automatic volume control is a common feature, and sometimes automatic mixing of music and commentary is available. All 8 mm magnetic projectors record at a standard picture to sound sync separation of 56 frames on standard 8 mm, and 18 frames on Super 8 mm. These systems usually allow only approximate synchronization, such as for mood music or commentary, and full *lip-sync*—that is, voices linked to the lip movements on the screen—is not possible.

Many amateurs increase the complexity of their soundtracks by following professional practice, shooting lip-sync dialogue scenes on reel-to-reel or cassette recorders, and recording a reference pulse track from the cine camera drive mechanism. Numerous devices are available for transferring the sound on to the striped picture film, and some equipment also allows for a limited amount of sound and picture editing, resulting in films which approach professional quality.

SPACE PROBES

Space probes are some of the most complicated robots devised, since they have to replace the abilities of man on long journeys through space to the Moon and planets and, on arriving at their destination, have to act as eyes and senses to detect what is there. An Earth SATELLITE sends back measurements and sometimes photographs of the terrain below it, but a space probe must often carry out precise manoeuvres when at a vast distance from Earth. Probes have been sent to the Moon, Mars, Venus, Mercury, Jupiter and Saturn; they have orbited the Sun to investigate conditions in space on the far side of Earth's orbit, so keeping the whole Sun under surveillance; and they have given simultaneous measurements of space particles at several points widely distributed through the solar system.

Design　The design of any space probe depends basically upon its destination and what it has to do. Almost all space probes and satellites have a fairly elementary framework around which can be added the various experiments and systems, and all probes of a particular class, such as the Mariners which were sent to Mercury, Venus and Mars, have basic similarities.

Near the Sun there are few problems of power supply; panels of solar cells will provide adequate supplies of electricity for several years. In the case of probes intended for Mars and beyond, however, the solar intensity is much lower and power from solar panels is limited.

In the case of the Pioneer craft destined for Jupiter and

Below: Pioneer 6, launched in 1965, is one of a series of probes designed to measure field strengths and particles in interplanetary space, giving information about the activity of the Sun at any time.

NASA

Left and above: both these pictures were taken by the same probe, Mariner 10. At left is Mercury, never previously seen as anything but a disc with vague shadings because of its proximity to the Sun, making it difficult to observe. On its way to Mercury, Mariner 10 flew past Venus, one of its pictures being shown above. Venus is completely cloud covered, so this picture was taken in ultra-violet light, revealing atmospheric circulation zones.

Saturn, no solar panels at all were used, since the solar intensity near Saturn is almost one hundredth of that near the Earth. Instead, four thermonuclear generators, producing heat from the RADIOACTIVE decay of plutonium-238 ISOTOPE, were used to provide 130 watts of power. This output deteriorates with time, and it seems likely that only about 80 watts will be available when Pioneer 11 encounters Saturn in 1979.

To protect the scientific instruments from radiation from these generators, the power units are located on booms pointing away from the instrument packages. Booms are often used on spacecraft where some particular instruments for collecting data, such as a MAGNETOMETER, may be affected by the others.

Another dominant feature of a space probe's design is the TELEMETRY antennae. The transmitter power is usually very low, of the order of a few watts, so to make the best use of it the signals must be beamed back to Earth by a parabolic dish reflector, which gives a narrow beam. In the case of Pioneer 10 and 11, this dish dominates the whole craft, being nine feet (2.7 m) in diameter. A low-gain 'spike' antenna is also provided for transmission at a low rate if the main beam is not exactly aligned with Earth. Very large parabolic dishes on Earth, such as NASA's Deep Space Network of dishes up to 210 feet (64 m) diameter, are needed to detect the very weak signals.

In order that the craft can point its antennae and experiments in the chosen direction, it must be *stabilized* in some way. The two methods available for any space vehicle are *spin stabilization* and *three axis stabilization*. In the former, the craft is set spinning by a platform on the launch vehicle just before it is sent on its way into space. Like a GYROSCOPE, it will

tend to stay spinning in the same direction in space. Where rapid pictures are to be taken and where a number of experiments have to be pointed in different directions, this is unsuitable. For most space probes, therefore, three axis stabilization is used in which the craft is kept in a particular orientation by means of attitude correctors. This means that the orientation of the craft must be known, and for this Sun and star *sensors* are employed to detect the direction of their chosen object. The Sun is easy to find as the brightest object in the sky, and one star only is needed to fix the orientation of the craft. The star Canopus, the second brightest in the sky, is generally used because of its brightness and its large angle from the Sun.

Minor effects, such as the gravitational pulls of the planets, may disturb the attitude. In this case, the attitude is corrected by means of small gas (usually nitrogen) jets. Another method, with the advantage that it does not deplete gas supplies, is to arrange a set of *reaction wheels* inside the spacecraft. By spinning one of these, the probe can be made to turn in the opposite direction at a rather slow rate.

The Pioneer probes, unlike most others, are spin stabilized. These craft are designed for long lifetimes: Pioneer 6, which became operational in 1965, has given many years service, and Pioneer 11, launched in 1973, is intended to encounter Saturn

Above: this photograph of the Moon's surface was taken from Lunar Orbiter 3, which in 1967 took 182 high resolution pictures from an orbit which at its lowest point was less than 35 miles altitude.

Right: Mariner 10 with its solar panels folded prior to launch. Its orbit, passing Venus and Mercury, was shown on page 1632 of How it Works. It made its third encounter with Mercury on 17 March 1975.

leaving the device to drop. The instruments were protected by being inside a ball-shaped capsule which was ejected from the main craft before impact to bounce and roll across the surface, coming to rest some distance away from the rocket. Four petals then opened out after an interval in such a way that the probe was forced upright and the instruments were revealed.

An improved technique was used by the Surveyor craft, five of which landed on the Moon in 1966 and 1967. These were equipped with controlled *vernier rockets* to keep the spacecraft attitude correct while the main retro-rocket slowed the craft down. This was then ejected and the vernier rockets took the spacecraft down to a soft landing. An essential feature of this technique is an automatic on-board controller linked to a radar ALTIMETER and velocity sensor working on the DOPPLER principle, which enables the craft to know how high above the surface it is and how fast it is moving. (Guidance from Earth would be difficult because of the $2\frac{1}{2}$ second delay in the round trip of a radio signal between Moon, Earth and Moon). This system is now standard for soft landing space probes. Subsequent probes, such as Luna 16, carried drills which took samples of the lunar surface. The upper part of the probe then used the lower part as a launching pad, and took off to return the samples to Earth.

Another device is the unmanned lunar rover, the Lunokhod series. These are carried aboard soft landing craft, and move about the Moon's surface under the control of a driver on Earth. The vehicles are equipped with such instruments as X-ray spectrometers for soil analysis, X-ray telescopes and television cameras which can show the driver where the rover is going and also return higher resolution pictures.

in 1979. The gas used in three axis stabilization could be used up on lengthy missions.

As well as correcting the attitude of craft, their ORBITS or paths through space have to be corrected from time to time. A probe in space will follow an ellipse round the Sun as predicted by KEPLER's Laws, unless its rocket is fired. This changes the orbit, and as soon as the rocket stops, the probe will continue along a new orbit, slightly different. These course correction manoeuvres are carefully calculated when the orbit of the probe is known, and if carried out accurately only one correction will be needed per mission. The craft is commanded to fire its rocket for a precise length of time at a certain instant. In this way extreme precision of aiming can be carried out.

Landers A number of space probes are designed not simply to travel past (*fly by*) a planet or to go into orbit around the planet, but have to land on the planet or on the Moon. Some of the earlier probes made little or no attempt to slow their velocity before striking the surface, and were known as *hard landers*. Some, such as the Ranger series, made no attempt to brake their progress and hit the Moon, taking television pictures as they went. Others, such as Luna 9 and Luna 13, had more of a 'rough landing' since their retro-rockets fired until they were very close to the lunar surface, then cut off

The Moon has no appreciable atmosphere, but the planets Mars and Venus have thin and thick atmospheres respectively. By using the atmospheres to slow down the craft, less fuel is needed for the descent. The Viking craft due to land on Mars in 1976, for example, descends on a parachute after preliminary rocket braking, and then carries out a powered landing using rockets with a large number of nozzles to spread the exhaust in an attempt to reduce soil erosion—of importance since the probe is designed to examine the Martian soil for possible traces of life.

The very thick atmosphere of Venus presents particular problems and no completely successful landing has so far been carried out. The atmospheric pressure at the surface of Venus is about 90 times that on Earth, the temperature is about 475°C (887°F) and there appear to be very strong convection currents. Succeeding craft have been made to withstand greater and greater pressures as previous craft failed before reaching the surface; Venera 7 apparently reached the surface

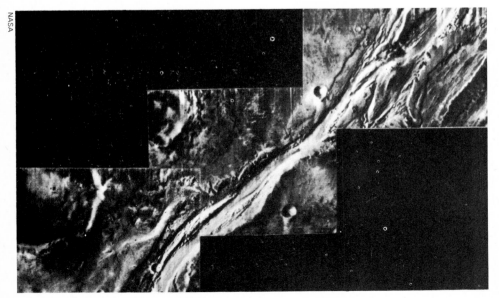

Above: Surveyor 3 landed on the Moon in 1967 and returned more than 6000 TV pictures of its surroundings prior to manned landings. In November 1969 the manned Apollo 12 module landed within 200 metres of Surveyor so that the state of the craft after 2½ years in the lunar environment could be examined.

Left: before Mariner 9's 1972 orbital flight, Mars was thought to be totally arid.
Pictures such as this raised hopes that water once flowed.

Top right: Pioneer 11 detail of Jupiter showing convection zones in this gas planet. All planets out to Jupiter have now been photographed in close up.

NASA

after a very rough parachute ride, and transmitted very faint signals for some 23 minutes. No rocket braking was used, and the craft seems to have struck the surface rather hard in the grip of a thermal current.

Instruments The point of sending space probes to the planets is to obtain details of conditions on the way and on arrival. The photographs sent back are the most spectacular results from probes, but scientific measurements of temperature, atmospheric pressure and composition, soil composition, magnetic field and particle densities are also made and sent back to Earth in the form of telemetry.

The cameras used for photography are not simple television cameras. The Moon probes Ranger and Surveyor had television cameras of special design, though neither returned the sort of continuous signals that normal broadcasting stations send out. Instead each picture took a short while to 'read' from the face of the camera tube. One reason for this is the *bandwidth* of the telemetry channel used: not enough information could be sent in the time needed.

The problems of insufficient bandwidth, coupled with the distance of the probe from Earth and low power supplies, have led to a variety of methods being used. The highest quality pictures ever sent back from space were from the Lunar Orbiter craft which orbited the Moon prior to the manned Apollo landings. True photographs were taken by a pair of cameras, and the film was then processed on board the spacecraft by bringing it into contact with a chemical-impregnated film. The pictures were then read out by a 'flying spot' of light, produced on the face of a CATHODE RAY TUBE which allowed the area of the photograph to be scanned as with a TV tube. The varying amount of light passing through the various parts of the film was picked up by a PHOTOMULTIPLIER TUBE and turned

into an electrical signal for return to Earth. The resulting photographs, when reconstituted, were sharp enough to reveal the grain structure of the original emulsion, and almost the whole lunar surface was mapped this way to a high resolution.

The Mariner craft sent to Mars, Venus and Mercury were equipped with tape recorders to record the camera output for later transmission at a slow rate. Mariner 9, for example, sent back a total of 7329 pictures of Mars over a period of a year from orbit. Two cameras, effectively small astronomical telescopes, were used with a variety of filters to measure colour and POLARIZATION of the surface. In addition, an infra-red *radiometer* or detector was aimed in the same direction as the cameras to measure the surface temperature. Similarly, a *spectrometer* (see SPECTROSCOPE) observed the infra-red absorption resulting from carbon dioxide, the main component of the thin Martian atmosphere. Areas where greatest carbon dioxide was observed and hence where the atmosphere was deepest, could therefore be linked with the photographs taken to decide the height of the surface at each particular point.

In the case of the spin-stabilized Pioneers 10 and 11, sent to Jupiter, the spinning of the spacecraft would have made normal photography difficult. Instead, an imaging device was set to view a mirror which slowly turned, reflecting the scene around the craft into the detector. As the probe spun on its axis, so a complete picture was built up in lines, like a TV picture. No cathode ray tubes or other television equipment were used, however. Each picture took between 25 and 110 minutes to build up, but in view of the great distance over which signals had to be sent, it would not have been possible to transmit pictures more rapidly anyway.

SPACE STATION (see orbital laboratory)

SPACESUIT

Our atmosphere on Earth gives us air, helps us to keep our body temperature constant and blocks out organically danger-ous radiation, and a human being venturing into the vacuum of space must take such an environment with him. This is part of the function of any manned space vehicle; reduce the spaceship to a personal level and you have the spacesuit. Such has been the approach taken to the design of suits worn by both Russian and American astronauts for all activities outside their spacecraft and for back-up protection within it. Space-suits are sometimes described as 'man-powered spacecraft'.

In spite of the absolute cold of space, almost −273°C (−459.4°F), solar rays are likely to overheat the spacesuit. Cooling is therefore highly important and the circulation of water through a network of tiny tubes has proved the most effective means of achieving this. The suit must also contain materials that make it completely airtight, flexible yet extremely tough, and resistant to solar radiation and micrometeoroids.

If, on an *extravehicular excursion* or 'spacewalk', the occupant is likely to remain close to the mother craft, then air and water can be circulated through an *umbilical hose*—like supplying a deep-sea diver through an air pipe. The umbilical also acts as a tether to stop the space-walker drifting away, and carries biomedical instrument links (to monitor such things as pulse rate) and communication links, plus electric power if the circulation pumps are attached to the suit rather than being in the mother craft.

For more remote activity such as lunar surface exploration, an independent supply plus associated machinery to operate it must all be carried by the wearer—paralleling the scuba diver—with the attendant limitation in endurance. Basic pressure

garments, plugged into main systems, have also been worn for security during critical phases of flight such as lift-off and re-entry by both Russians and Americans, the suit being totally or only partially worn according to variations in contemporary views of the risk. On one Russian mission, Voskhod 1, the three crewmen took no suits at all with them. After the accidental depressurization just before re-entry of Soyuz 11, which killed the three crewmen, Russia reinstated fully suited re-entries for a cautionary period.

Early suits Spacesuit technology has naturally developed along with that of other space hardware. Spacesuits are all made to measure, as befitting such complex garments, often incorporating minor preferences of the wearer such as the positions of the pockets. Each man has, in fact, three suits, including one for reserve and one for ground training. The relatively simple pressure suit worn by Alan Shepard on the first US suborbital flight, however, bears little resemblance to the highly complex equipment worn by the lunar explorers.

For example, the crews of America's early two-man Gemini flights wore pressure suits against cabin depressurization but not designed for extravehicular activity. These suits had five

Right: the type of suit worn on the Apollo moon missions. There is no provision for the disposal of solid body wastes within the suit, but urine can be disposed of by means of a 'fitted receptacle' with a tube leading to a small tank in the right leg of the suit, which is emptied later into a container or an overboard discharge system.

Below: an Apollo 17 astronaut taking samples of soil from the surface of the Moon. The backpack is his Personal Life Support System which enables him to work away from the lunar module.

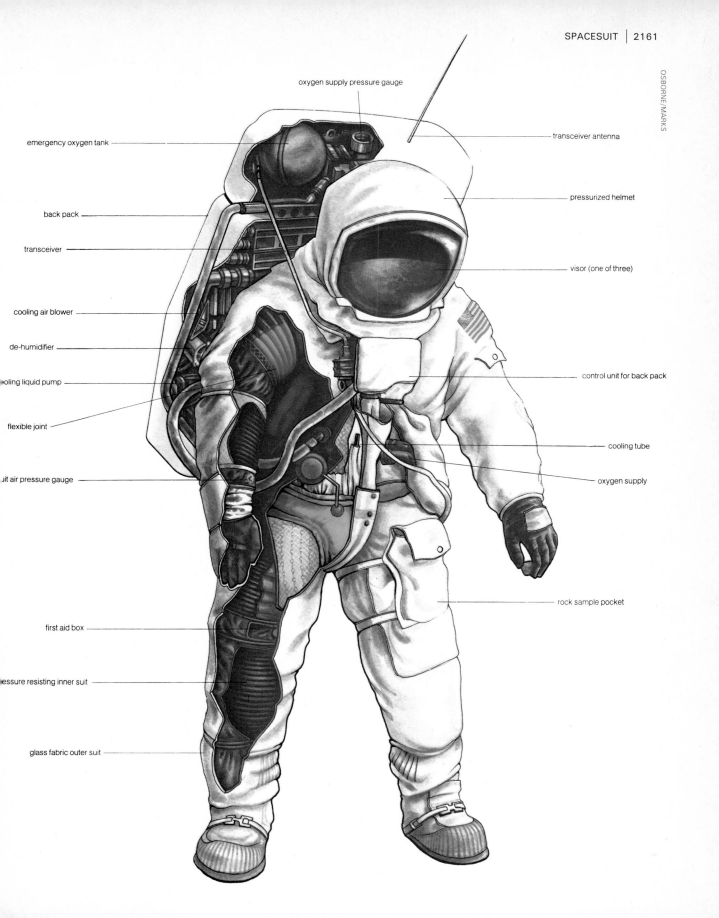

oxygen supply pressure gauge

emergency oxygen tank

transceiver antenna

pressurized helmet

back pack

transceiver

visor (one of three)

cooling air blower

de-humidifier

cooling liquid pump

control unit for back pack

flexible joint

cooling tube

oxygen supply

suit air pressure gauge

rock sample pocket

first aid box

pressure resisting inner suit

glass fabric outer suit

layers, beginning with white cotton underwear with attachments for biomedical instruments. Next came a blue nylon layer, purely for comfort, and then a pressure garment of black neoprene-coated nylon, which pressurized at 3.5 psi (0.24 bar) of pure oxygen if cabin pressure failed. Over this was a link-net layer of Dacron coated Teflon to hold the suit's shape when pressurized, and it was topped by a white HT-1 nylon layer to guard against accidental damage and reflected sunshine.

A new 16 lb (7.3 kg) lightweight suit was introduced just for Gemini 7, composed simply of a neoprene nylon inner layer with HT-1 nylon on top, plus an ordinary pilot's helmet under a soft pressure hood.

Gemini space walks required extra protection which resulted in a seven-layer garment. Two extra layers, aluminized Mylar for thermal protection and a micrometeoroid protective layer, were inserted under the top layer of the basic five-piece suit. The total weight was 33 lb (15 kg)—of little significance in gravity-free orbit.

Apollo suits Apollo suits were even more complicated. When not in spacesuits, Apollo crew wore only light two-piece Teflon fabric overalls. The Command Module Pilot, who remained in the Apollo CM throughout the flight except for a brief spacewalk, required a simple five-layer pressure garment. But the lunar surface walkers wore two additional garments, plus a life-support backpack, all adding up to an Earth weight of 57 lb (26 kg). A modified version of this suit (without backpack) was also used by Skylab crews for outdoor activities.

The undergarment resembles long underwear and contains the cooling-water circulation tubing. Then comes the neoprene-coated pressure garment. On top, however, is an 18-layer 'integrated thermal meteoroid suit'. This begins with rubber-coated nylon and then non-woven Dacron, then aluminized Mylar film and Beta marquisette (a woven fabric) layers to inhibit heat radiation. On top is a layer of non-flammable Teflon-coated Beta cloth and finally an abrasion-resistant layer of Teflon fabric. The boots contain an even more diverse assemblage of materials. The helmet has two visors which together shield it against heat, ultra-violet and infra-red radiation and micrometeoroids. A tube leads into the helmet from a 2 pint (1.14 litre) water bag inside the suit neck ring. Finally, there is the self-descriptive Personal Life Support System, or backpack—a highly engineered unit which gives the wearer autonomy and security. In the terminology of NASA, the US space agency, it is then no longer a spacesuit, it is an *Extravehicular Mobility Unit*.

Below left: James Irwin comparing the ease of motion of an original Apollo pressure suit, on the left, to the newer improved version on the right worn by John Bull. Several of the changes made to the suit design can be seen in this photograph, and the new suit also has a layer of beta fabric, a non-flammable glass fibre cloth.

Below right: a Russian space suit, with backpack, which was used on the three-man Soyuz flights.

SPACE VEHICLES

The comparative novelty of space travel means that both American and Russian manned space activities have so far merely subsisted, relatively speaking, on makeshift equipment devised to master the basic knowledge and technology and to achieve certain limited objectives such as short one-stop visits to the Moon. In most respects a manned spacecraft compares in description with any unmanned SATELLITE or SPACE PROBE, but on a larger scale. Once basic technology is established, man's role becomes that of a far more efficient trouble-shooter and robot operator than we are yet capable of devising. His presence, however, demands additional expensive safety measures such as back-up systems and extra testing as well as large-scale hardware and complex life-support systems. The argument still rages as to whether the advantages merit the expense. The policy of NASA, the US space agency, is that manned and unmanned craft can be complementary and that both capabilities must be developed, but costed carefully.

Any manned space vehicle has certain fundamental requirements. It must have a powerful main ROCKET engine, preferably controllable, to perform course corrections, manoeuvres in Earth or lunar orbit and deorbiting retro-fire, plus sufficient reserve propellant. Today's fuels would be prohibitively bulky in the quantities required for long-duration missions and revolutionary rocket techniques using nuclear energy or ionized gases (see IONIC PROPULSION) are under development for the spaceships of tomorrow.

It must also have an assembly of attitude-control *thrusters* (small rocket motors) to perform the same task as the ailerons, rudder and elevator of an aircraft. Usually duplicated for safety, thrusters are paired diametrically in opposition to apply torque (twisting force) round the appropriate axis. Each set of thrusters has its own fuel tanks and all are controlled by a joystick which electronically selects thrusters to control the craft in the same sense as an aircraft.

Systems   Most systems depend on electric power, which was provided in early craft by short-life batteries. NASA introduced FUEL CELLS in Gemini and Apollo, generating power by conversion of oxygen and hydrogen into drinkable water. Russia's Soyuz depends on solar generator panels of older technological vintage. Miniature nuclear generators, already used on some probes, are now becoming practicable for very lengthy manned missions.

Temperature control is important because, in space, the craft is cooked on one side by the Sun and chilled on the other by space. The loss of a solar panel on Skylab (see ORBITAL LABORATORY) meant insufficient power to operate cooling systems properly, hence the need to erect a sunshield. During translunar flight, the Apollo craft distributes heat by spinning slowly in what is termed the 'barbecue mode'.

Pressurization depends on sufficient air supplies to cope with normal consumption plus any cabin repressurizations required for space excursions. Air, water and food present a severe weight penalty and future flights of any length will

Left: the expended Saturn 4-B stage of the launch vehicle for the Skylab-3 mission. American rockets are launched on a trajectory which takes them over the Atlantic Ocean, so the burnt-out first stage, jettisoned at a height of 30 to 50 miles (48 to 80 km), falls harmlessly into the sea. Subsequent stages, depending on the height at which they separate, either burn up in the atmosphere or go into Earth orbit.

Below: a Soyuz command module, which carries a crew of three, on display at an exhibition in Moscow. The first Soyuz mission flew in April 1967, but the single crewman was killed when it crash-landed.

PHOTRI

IAN RIDPATH

probably have to recycle such consumables either mechanically or ecologically (using plants). The Russians have consistently used an Earth-type atmosphere of oxygen and nitrogen at near sea-level pressure. US craft have all relied on pure oxygen at only 5 psi (0.345 bar), except that Apollos have used an Earth atmosphere for launch and then converted to oxygen in orbit. This is a precaution taken after pure oxygen fuelled a fire that broke out in the spacecraft cabin during launchpad tests in preparation for the first manned Apollo mission, killing astronauts Gus Grissom, Ed White and Roger Chaffee.

Communications are the lifeline with Earth. Future spaceships will have considerable computer capacity to monitor their own systems, and future technology will have earned greater confidence. But today, a very large number of systems has to be monitored constantly from Earth, including crew health. In addition, voice and television channels must be maintained reliably and at adequate strength with limited on-board power, so there is a need for highly directional aerials operating on microwave frequencies.

Finally, the manned craft must have a means of returning its occupants to Earth. The severe conditions of atmospheric re-entry have dictated a modular approach to vehicles so far, in order to minimize the amount of vehicle requiring a special shape and covering to protect it from the 3000°F (1650°C) generated by the friction of the air at 17,000 mph (27,360 km/h). Capsules have been conical to let most of the surface hide behind the heat shield, or slightly curved as with Soyuz to improve aerodynamic lift and ease deceleration loads. The blunt heat shield is necessary to brake the craft to parachute-deployment speed. Heat shields have depended on *ablation* techniques whereby a thick plastic coating is allowed to burn

Above left: astronaut David R Scott during extravehicular activity on the fourth day of the Apollo 9 Earth-orbital mission. Scott is standing in the open hatch of the command module.

Above: the Apollo 15 command and service modules in lunar orbit over the Sea of Fertility in 1971. The service module instrument bay is open to permit scientific studies of the Moon from orbit.

off and dissipate the heat. A thinner coating is applied to all other surfaces.

Early vehicles In present day terms, 'spaceship' means Mercury, Gemini and Apollo on the US side and Vostok (East), Voskhod (Sunrise) and Soyuz (Union) on the Soviet side. As comparative evolutionary steps, the three can be matched up only in numbers of crewmen, having more or less leapfrogged each other in terms of technical advance.

As the space age dawned the true potential of the unmanned satellite had yet to reveal itself, and as Man saw himself as the key to space exploration, research on manned spaceflight began early. Russia's second Sputnik carried a dog ('Laika') irretrievably into orbit. Five dog-carrying craft preceded the first ever manned space flight when, on April 12 1961, Yuri Gagarin made a single orbit of the Earth. Soviet experience was extended over the next two years by five more Vostok flights, the last carrying Valentina Tereshkova, the first and only woman in space by 1975.

Vostok comprised a spherical re-entry capsule and a cylindrical service module containing the retro-engine and more subsystems. Designed purely to achieve basic techniques of orbiting and recovery of manned craft, it carried ten days' battery power and was intended for full ground control,

OSBORNE/MARKS

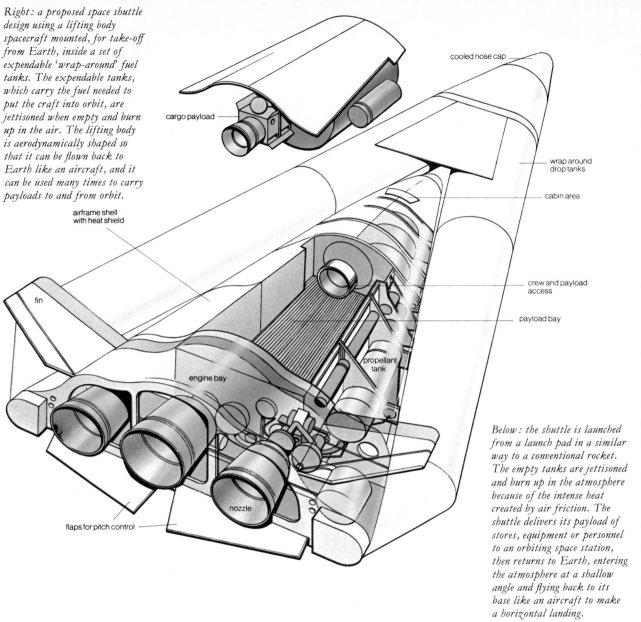

Right: a proposed space shuttle design using a lifting body spacecraft mounted, for take-off from Earth, inside a set of expendable 'wrap-around' fuel tanks. The expendable tanks, which carry the fuel needed to put the craft into orbit, are jettisoned when empty and burn up in the air. The lifting body is aerodynamically shaped so that it can be flown back to Earth like an aircraft, and it can be used many times to carry payloads to and from orbit.

cooled nose cap

cargo payload

wrap around drop tanks

cabin area

crew and payload access

payload bay

airframe shell with heat shield

propellant tank

fin

engine bay

nozzle

flaps for pitch control

Below: the shuttle is launched from a launch pad in a similar way to a conventional rocket. The empty tanks are jettisoned and burn up in the atmosphere because of the intense heat created by air friction. The shuttle delivers its payload of stores, equipment or personnel to an orbiting space station, then returns to Earth, entering the atmosphere at a shallow angle and flying back to its base like an aircraft to make a horizontal landing.

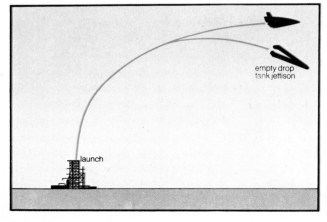

launch

empty drop tank jettison

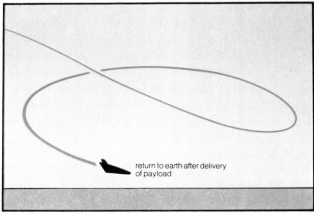

return to earth after delivery of payload

although equipped for basic pilot control.

America used chimpanzees for preparatory work, including a suborbital Mercury trial preceding each of two manned suborbital flights. A chimp was then orbited before John Glenn made America's first orbital flight on February 20 1962. Three more manned flights completed the programme.

Mercury was a simple bell-shaped craft, double-walled like all US manned vehicles, the outer wall being made of nickel alloy and the inner of titanium. Ceramic fibre insulated the walls while the heat shield was covered in a glass fibre and resin mixture. All subsystems were located within the pressurized capsule itself, minimizing size and weight for the limited US launch capability of the time. Retro-thrust was provided by a package of three solid-fuel rockets strapped to the heat shield.

A major difference between the two craft, and one that set that pattern for all subsequent vehicles, was that the Russians opted for land recovery while the Americans preferred water, in spite of the massive recovery operations necessary (John Glenn received the services of 24 ships and 126 aircraft). Techniques had been perfected enough by the later Apollo flights to reduce this to a handful of ships and aircraft. Without the cushion of water, Vostok touchdowns were possibly quite heavy because, except for the first (Gagarin's) mission, the crewmen always used an EJECTION SEAT at 23,000 ft (7 km) and landed separately.

The next step involved two Russian flights called Voskhod, the first carrying three men, the second only two. General evidence plus a lack of pictures suggests that these were modified Vostoks designed (successfully) to upstage the Americans. In Voskhod 1, space for the two extra seats meant omitting ejection seats and spacesuits. With its spacewalk objective, Voskhod 2 required spacesuits and an airlock, hence the two man crew.

Planning for the Apollo Moon landing programme had already begun even before the first Mercury flight, but the two-year Gemini programme of 10 two man flights was introduced to develop essential rendezvous and docking, long duration and space walking expertise. Basically an enlarged and improved Mercury, Gemini comprised a main re-entry module plus the launch vehicle adapter section used as an unpressurized bay for life-support and power-supply equipment, and was constructed largely of titanium and magnesium. It was the first craft to carry a computer, enabling variations in flight plan to be calculated. Ejection seats substituted for a launch escape tower (a small rocket fitted on top of the command module to pull it away from the launch vehicle in case of emergency), hence separate hatches were needed for each crewman.

Soyuz It is presumed that lunar applications were intended for the three man Soyuz which first flew in April 1967, but

Top: an astronaut on the Apollo 12 Moon mission in November 1969 setting up a nuclear powered generator next to the lunar module descent stage.

Left: the Apollo 11 lunar module, which carried the first men to land on the Moon. Neil Armstrong stepped out of the module on to the surface of the Moon on 20 July 1969.

Right: James Irwin with the Apollo 15 Lunar Rover Vehicle in 1971. The vehicle was driven a total of 17·3 miles (28 km), and about 168 pounds (76 kg) of lunar rock and soil were collected.

unfortunately crash-landed, killing the single crewman, Vladimir Komarov. Objectives seem to have veered towards space stations in 1969 when it became apparent that an American lunar landing was imminent. Several subsequent flights, expanding on Gemini-type activities, culminated in the launch and manning of the first Salyut orbital laboratory in April 1971. Soyuz 11, which docked with Salyut in June 1971, ended fatally for the crew, Georgi Dobrovolsky, Viktor Patsayev and Vladislav Volkov, when their ship accidentally depressurized during re-entry. Since then, Soyuz flights have continued in connection with follow-on Salyuts and towards the joint US-USSR rendezvous and docking mission planned for 1975.

Soyuz consists of three sections, a spherical orbital module, in the nose, behind which is an igloo-shaped re-entry compartment and a cylindrical service module in the rear to which a pair of 12 ft (3.7 m) long solar panels are attached. The orbital module is a general utility compartment containing working, eating and sleeping facilities. It has a main entry hatch, and a connecting hatch to the re-entry module so that it also serves as an airlock for space excursions.

The re-entry module has its three crew couches arranged fanwise to fit the confined space, and its heat shield contains a small solid-fuel rocket which fires at 3 ft (1 m) altitude to cushion touchdown. The service module contains most of the subsystems, including two liquid fuel engines (one spare) and fuel for manoeuvring up to 800 miles (1287 km) altitude.

Apollo Apollo was basically designed, in conjunction with the lunar module, to take three men to the Moon and back and to achieve little more. The conical command module, made of stainless steel sandwich containing stainless steel honeycomb, uses a phenolic epoxy resin on its ablative heat shield. A docking probe in the nose is removable (along with the lunar module's corresponding drogue) after connections are secure, to provide a clear tunnel between the two craft. The cylindrical service module contains the 20,500 lb (9300 kg) thrust main engine used for all manoeuvres. It also carries propellants for main engine and thrusters, plus oxygen and hydrogen for fuel cells and life support.

The Apollo lunar module (LM) was the first true spaceship, in being devoid of any aerodynamic characteristics. An octagonal descent stage carried the main engine and fuel, air and water supplies and general equipment for the surface stay. As the descent stage was not needed for the return flight, it was abandoned, serving as a launch pad for the multifaceted ascent stage which contained the pressurized two man cabin and all systems of a spacecraft in its own right.

The last three Apollo missions used much-modified craft, enormously extending the mission capabilities. The mother ship carried a complex package of scientific instruments, exposed from one section of the service module for orbital study of the Moon, plus more supplies for extended flight time. The LM was similarly improved to allow not only for a three

NASA

day surface stay but also for three complete cabin repressurizations as well. In addition it carried a lunar roving vehicle (LRV).

The LRV, or 'rover', was a fold-up, two seat car in which the astronauts were able to explore extensively the landing zone. As such, it was the forerunner of what will be an essential adjunct of future manned exploration of the planets. Its two 36 V batteries provided one hp from motors located on each of the four wheels for up to 57 miles (92 km) at up to 8.7 mph (14 km/h). It was equipped with INERTIAL NAVIGATION and carried an Earth controlled TV camera so that controllers could direct their own observations.

The future   The next step will be NASA's space shuttle, a reusable manned freighter plying regularly between Earth and low orbit on a wide variety of missions. Evidence suggests that the Russians are also developing a similar type of vehicle. The shuttle is significant because it represents the beginnings of a practical maturity in manned space activities.

The shuttle will be similar to a conventional aircraft launched vertically and returning unpowered to a runway landing. Instead of ablative protection it will be covered with a new type of ceramic tile designed for repeated use. It will lift off on its three liquid-fuelled engines, fed from a huge external belly tank to which a pair of solid fuel boosters are attached, providing the bulk of lift-off thrust. The boosters will be jettisoned at altitude and recovered from the ocean for reuse. The fuel tank will be discarded from orbit for destruction in the atmosphere. Two smaller engines will provide orbital manoeuvring.

The shuttle is mostly cargo bay—60 ft by 15 ft (18.3 m by 4.6 m) in size and capable of taking up to 65,000 lb (29,500 kg) into orbit or bringing 40,000 lb (18,144 kg) back to Earth. So it will not only lay satellites but also recover them for repair or renovation. Fortnightly flights will be possible with a crew of four and there will be room for four passengers. This is so that scientists can be carried to work in a new modular orbital laboratory payload called Spacelab (being developed in Europe), and turning the shuttle into a versatile orbital laboratory for periods of 7 to 30 days.

The next step will be the permanent space station, assembled and serviced with the shuttle. A robot tug is being built to augment the shuttle by boosting payloads to orbits higher than the shuttle's limits. This could well evolve into a manned space tug which would be the first proper spaceship, operating permanently in space. When money permits further lunar exploration or building a lunar surface station, it will become a translunar ferry, connecting with the shuttle or space station in Earth orbit.

The interplanetary spaceship is already a theoretical reality. A manned Mars mission, now shelved, had been planned by NASA to begin in 1986. The two year round trip was to have involved two identical six man vessels (for mutual support) assembled in orbit. As conceived, each ship was to consist of four huge cylinders, three in a row as propellant tanks for three nuclear engines, plus a crew section projecting end on from the central tank, its forward end slightly splayed to accommodate landing craft. Its length was 270 ft (82.3 m), its weight 1.6 million lb (0.73 million kg).

The two outer engines would have provided initial boost before being detached and returned to Earth orbit. The third was to power the remainder of the voyage. The ships were to remain in Mars orbit for 80 days, with half of each crew spending 30 days on the surface. Fuel limitations meant a 290 day return journey, crossing Earth's orbit in order to use the gravity of Venus to swing the craft back to Earth.

SPARK PLUG

Spark plugs are used in most INTERNAL COMBUSTION ENGINES (except DIESEL ENGINES) to provide the high voltage sparks which ignite the fuel-air mixture in the combustion chambers. The invention of spark plugs is attributed to Etienne Lenoir (1822–1900), who in 1860 first manufactured an engine which used an electric spark IGNITION SYSTEM.

Operation   When the engine is running, a pulse of electrical energy at very high voltage is delivered to the terminal of the plug (or plugs in the case of multi-cylinder engines, via the DISTRIBUTOR) at the correct moment. This causes a spark to jump the gap between the centre electrode and the earth [ground] electrode, the latter being earthed to the cylinder block. This spark provides the energy needed to ignite the compressed fuel-air mixture in the cylinder.

Operating temperature   For optimum performance, the temperature of the core nose at the firing end of a spark plug should neither drop below about 400°C (752°F) at 30 mph (48 km/h) cruising, nor exceed about 850°C (1562°F) at maximum speed and load. Below 400°C, deposits of carbon and oil are likely to accumulate on the core nose. Carbon, being electrically conductive, can provide a short circuit path for the high voltage pulse and so weaken or eliminate the spark.

Core nose temperatures of above 850°C can cause excessive electrode erosion and, possibly, uncontrolled ignition of the fuel-air mixture in advance of the timed spark. This condition (called *pre-ignition*) can cause serious engine damage.

As engine designs (and therefore combustion chamber

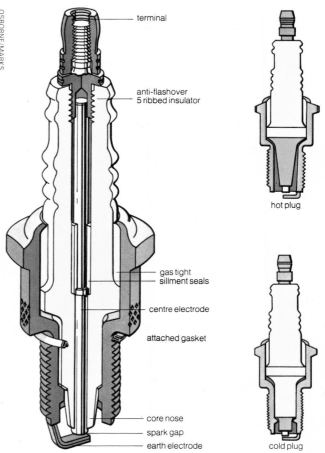

terminal

anti-flashover
5 ribbed insulator

gas tight
sillment seals

centre electrode

attached gasket

core nose
spark gap
earth electrode

hot plug

cold plug

temperatures) vary, it is necessary to produce many types of spark plug to ensure that, as far as possible, plug operating temperatures can be kept within the optimum range in all applications.

Heat range   The classification of plugs according to their relative ability to transfer heat from the tip of the core nose to the cooling system of an engine is termed the *heat range*.

A 'hot' (or 'soft') plug has a relatively long core nose, and thus a long heat path from the tip to the metal body. This type of plug tends to retain heat in the core nose, and would be used in a low compression, low speed engine.

Conversely, a 'cold' (or 'hard') plug has a shorter core nose, giving a shorter heat path from the tip to the body, and heat is conducted rapidly from the core nose into the cooling medium. This type is used in high compression, high speed engines having higher combustion chamber temperatures.

In order to determine which grade of plug is best for a particular engine design, manufacturers run tests using spark plugs which incorporate thermocouples (temperature sensing elements) at the core nose tips. During the tests, the core nose temperatures of various grades of plug are continuously monitored throughout the entire speed and load range of the engine.

Projected core nose plugs   In recent years there has been an enormous increase in the use of plugs on which the core nose projects beyond the end of the threaded body. This design of plug is specified only for overhead valve engines with suitable combustion chamber design. The extra-long core nose runs hotter than a standard type at low engine speeds, giving improved protection against plug fouling. At high engine speeds the exposed core nose tip is cooled by the incoming feel-air mixture; this avoids the risk of plug overheating. Projected core nose plugs are used in the vast majority of modern overhead valve engines.

Manufacture   Design techniques and materials used vary from one manufacturer to another, but the following description is fairly representative.

Plug bodies are made of high quality steel, and are zinc plated to avoid corrosion. The threads (which are *rolled*, see SCREW MANUFACTURE) have to conform to internationally agreed standards and close tolerances. Ranges of plugs with various thread configurations are produced.

The plug insulators are made from a fired aluminium oxide CERAMIC MATERIAL which is highly resistant to thermal and mechanical stress and chemical attack. The electrodes are most commonly made from nickel alloys, but precious metals are sometimes used.

Gas-tight seals are required between the centre electrode and the insulator, and between the insulator and the plug body. These seals are formed from aluminium oxide powder (termed *sillment*) which, when compressed, becomes a rigid mass which fits the available space exactly. A pre-formed lip around the top of the body is squeezed downwards on to the compacted sillment seal.

To keep pace with engine requirements, new construction techniques and materials are constantly being evaluated.

Right: cutaway of a spark plug which has been modified to incorporate a thermocouple to enable core nose temperatures to be monitored. The wires that connect the thermocouple are on either side of the centre electrode, and the thermocouple itself is just above the lower end of the core nose.

Far right: effects of various operating conditions on spark plugs. From top to bottom: normal running; carbon fouled, due to over-rich mixture and too large a plug gap; oil fouled, due to too much oil in the combustion chamber; and an overheated plug.

Left: the large drawing shows the component parts of a modern spark plug. The high voltage pulse of electricity passes down the centre electrode and jumps across the spark gap to the earth [ground] electrode. The smaller drawings show the difference between the core nose lengths of 'hot' and 'cold' plugs, the 'hot' plug having a much longer core nose than the 'cold' one.

SPEAKING CLOCK

The speaking clock is a system for providing an accurate time announcement over the public TELEPHONE network. It is an extremely reliable system consisting of two independent announcement machines which are run in synchronism. Should either machine get out of step or stop, the other machine takes over completely while the first is repaired.

In Britain alone, over 100 million calls a year are made to this service. The British system provides an announcement, based on the 12 hour clock, of the form: 'at the third stroke, it will be five, twenty-three, and forty seconds', followed by three pips of 1 kHz tones. Announcements are made every ten seconds. Twenty-four hour clocks are available and in use in many countries, but the system is basically unaltered.

Description of the system

The announcements are recorded on a magnetic drum. This consists of a brass cylinder overlaid with a neoprene film impregnated with a magnetic material (iron oxide). Because of the repetitive nature of time announcements, only 79 separate phrases need be recorded for a 12 hour clock: the initial phrase 'at the third stroke' plus 12 hour phrases 'it will be . . .', 60 minutes (o'clock plus 1 to 59) and 6 second numbers (10, 20, 30, 40, 50, and 'precisely' for the exact minute). These 79 phrases are recorded as separate tracks on the drum at $\frac{1}{16}$ inch (1.6 mm) intervals.

The tracks are arranged in four groups: the initial phrase is 'read' by a fixed head. The hours are read by a head which is stepped once every hour. The minute tracks are split into four sub-groups of 15 phrases with four read heads which are stepped together once every four minutes. A secondary selector mechanism selects each of the four heads in sequence. The operating sequence for the minutes is: o'clock, 1, 2, 3,—shift heads—4, 5, 6, 7,—shift heads—and so on up to 56, 57, 58, 59. The six seconds tracks each have their own fixed reading heads, but here again, a selector mechanism is required to select each head in sequence.

Drive mechanism

The drum, head movements, selector mechanisms and the three pips are controlled by the drive motor. This is a synchronous electric motor which runs at 1500 rpm using a 50 Hz power supply. As no phrase is longer than two seconds the drum is made to rotate at precisely one revolution every two seconds (30 rpm). The drum is therefore linked to the motor via a gear mechanism with a reduction ratio of 50:1. Further gearing controls the head movement, selector mechanisms and the pips.

The reliability of the machine depends on the motor speed. The 50 Hz supply to this is therefore controlled by a quartz crystal OSCILLATOR.

Quartz oscillator

The quartz crystal oscillator is temperature controlled to provide a very stable 100 kHz sine wave. By suitable dividing circuitry, this frequency is reduced first to 1 kHz (see QUARTZ CLOCK). This provides the pip tone.

Right: one of the two speaking clock mechanisms that are run in synchronism. The phrase and seconds heads are fixed but hour and minute heads are moved by lever and cam from a stepping gearbox. Lines in blue indicate that relevant components of the speech (and pips) are present—switching in and out of relevant components is achieved by cams and contacts (shown with pushrods for clarity).

Below: the early speaking clock mechanism which was introduced into Britain in 1936. Glass discs were used to record the announcements which were controlled by a temperature stabilized pendulum.

OSBORNE/MARKS

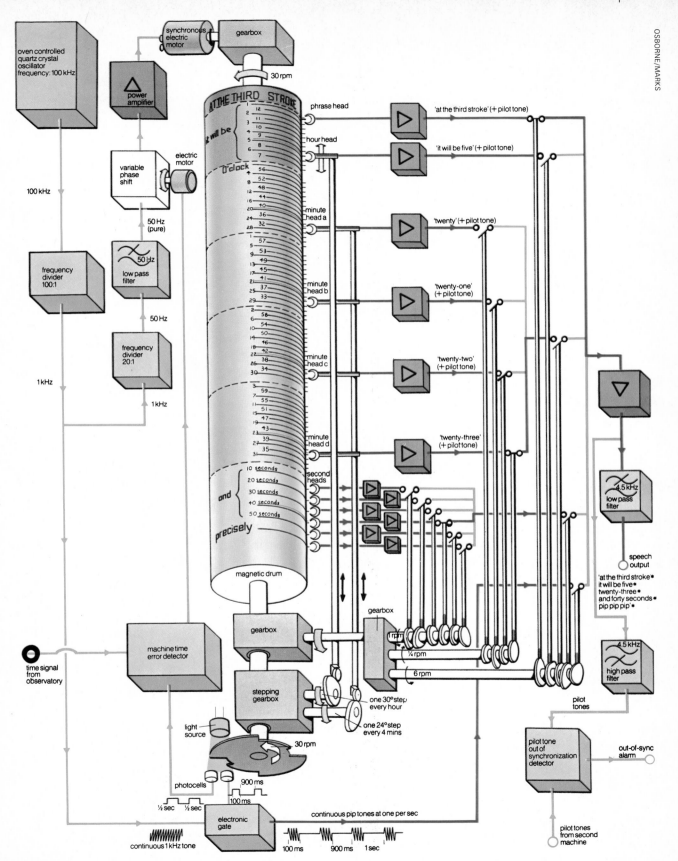

The two announcement machines have their own oscillators, but are under constant surveillance to make sure they remain in synchronism. Further dividers reduce this 1 kHz frequency to 50 Hz as the source for the synchronous drive motor.

The pips

The pips consist of three 100 ms (0.1 second) bursts of 1 kHz frequency at one second intervals. This is achieved by an electronic 'gate' on the 1 kHz frequency line which opens for 100 ms every second. The signal to open this gate is derived from a PHOTOELECTRIC CELL. A beam of light is focused on the cell with a rotating shutter in between linked directly to the rotating drum (speed 30 rpm). Two slots are positioned in the shutter so that twice every revolution (that is, once per second) light strikes the cell and turns the gate on. The periphery of this shutter has extended slots to provide a 1 Hz square wave ($\frac{1}{2}$ second on, $\frac{1}{2}$ second off) from a second photoelectric cell which is used to adjust the drive motor should the crystal oscillator drift over a period of time.

Time correction

The two machines are ultimately controlled by an ATOMIC CLOCK which, in Britain, is situated in the Royal Observatory at Herstmonceux in Sussex. The machines are corrected once a day. Time signals from the Observatory arrive in the form of 100 ms pulses every second. If the 1 Hz square wave pulses generated by either of the machines is out of phase with the Observatory signal, a correction signal is generated which turns a small motor. This motor is linked to a phase-shift device that can shift the phase of the 50 Hz supply to the drive motor. One complete rotation of the phase-shifter advances or retards the 50 Hz supply by one cycle—that is, by 20 ms. In this way, each machine is monitored separately, but to make sure that the two machines are running in synchronism other surveillance mechanisms are employed.

Synchronization

Should either of the machines develop a fault, the other must take over immediately. Consequently, they must run in perfect synchronism. Two systems are provided to make sure this is so.

On each of the 79 tracks are also recorded pilot tones of 5.5 kHz, 6.5 or 7.5 kHz. These tones are constantly monitored between the two machines so if they get out of step an alarm is given. A low pass FILTER removes these tones from the speech output.

The 100 kHz crystal oscillator frequencies are also monitored. If they are different, a beat frequency can be detected, and if this is significant an alarm is operated. In Britain, the Post Office provides a standard 1 kHz frequency, and by multiplying this up to 100 kHz, the two machines' oscillators can also be checked against standard time by detecting the beat frequencies.

History

The speaking clock service has been provided in Britain since 1936. The early devices, although in principle the same as the modern system, used four glass discs with photographically recorded tracks (similar to record discs). A pendulum swinging freely in a temperature controlled cabinet was the forerunner of the quartz oscillator. Corrections were made hourly to these early machines from the Royal Observatory, thus maintaining their accuracy to within 100 ms (0.1 second).

The modern machines, by comparison, are far more accurate. The oscillators are accurate to within 5 ms (0.005 second) with an extra inaccuracy of 1 ms introduced by the motor and gears. The correction mechanism itself will only operate when differences greater than 4 ms are detected, so the maximum error before correction is 10 ms.

Surprisingly, the main error in this system is now not the system itself, but the very nature of TIME. Although the machines are accurate to within 10 ms of atomic time, fluctuations in the rotation of the Earth, to which our notion of real time must be related, make the machines accurate to within only 50 ms (0.05 s). Adjustment to Universal Time (UT), based on the Earth's rotation, is made once every month.

Left: a modern speaking clock system consisting of two independent mechanisms side by side—these are run in synchronism and provide a failsafe system. The cabinets in the background house the two oven-controlled quartz crystal oscillators and alarm mechanisms.

Below: general layout of the speaking clock mechanism. The motor (left) drives the drum 'read' head-shift cams and contact selector mechanisms via gears. There are twelve read heads altogether.

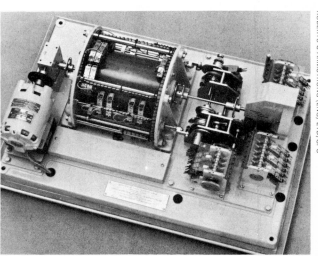

SPECIAL EFFECTS

The term 'special effects' is a blanket one that covers many of the techniques used in the production of cinematic illusions. It was first introduced by effects man Louis Witts in 1926 on the Hollywood film *What Price Glory?* Special effects can be divided into two main categories: *visual* or *optical* effects, and *physical* or *mechanical* effects. Visual effects mainly involve photographic processes, while physical effects consist of things such as explosions, car crashes and so on.

History Trick photography is as old as the cinema itself. In fact, most of the early films *were* trick films. The cinema, for at least a decade after its beginning in 1895, was considered solely as a novelty and the film makers of that era concentrated on producing films that were as technically inventive as possible and, in doing so, pioneered many of the effects techniques that are still in use today. British innovators in the field include G A Smith, who took out a patent for a double exposure technique in 1897, and Robert William Paul who, also in 1897, built in London what was probably Europe's first film studio and equipped it to produce a wide range of trick films.

The name most associated with early trick films is that of Frenchman Georges Méliès, a former stage magician who was so impressed by the first demonstration of moving pictures projected on to a screen, given by the LUMIERE brothers in Paris in 1895, that he decided to start making his own films. He employed many of the techniques used by stage magicians as well as pioneering motion picture techniques such as jump cuts, fast and slow motion, dissolves, fades, double exposure and multiple exposure. American pioneer Edwin S Porter was greatly influenced by Méliès and produced many trick films for the Edison Company, but in 1903 he made *The Great Train Robbery*, one of the first films to tell a story. Thus, ironically,

he was responsible for bringing the era of the pure trick film to an end. Trick effects continued to be used in silent films, but only to complement the story, rarely for their own sake. In fact, in the 1920s, cinema audiences were resentful whenever they detected any use of special effects, preferring to think that the spectacular action they saw upon the screen was all real (and owing to the dangerous risks that stuntmen took in those days, such as actually crashing aircraft into buildings, it often *was* real). For many years the use of models, double exposures and so on was considered by audiences to be cheating and it was not until fantasy and science fiction films became popular in the 1930s that the blatant use of special effects became acceptable again, such as in *The Invisible Man* series.

Trick photography The basic techniques of trick photography make use of the nature of movie film, in which each frame lasts for only a fraction of a second on the screen and the persistence of vision of the human eye gives the impression of continuous movement. In the *jump cut*, for example, the camera is stopped and some change is made to the scene being photographed—an actor may move out of view, or a fake prop may be substituted for a real one. If well done, and if the camera is not moved or the lighting changed, the eye will be fooled into believing that the action was continuous. *Dissolves* and *fades* are now carried out in the laboratory, but in the early days (and in modern amateur productions) were carried out in the camera. One scene is faded out by reducing the exposure, the film is wound back, and the second scene is faded in by increasing its exposure from zero, creating the

The mirror shot was invented in the '20s to combine models and live action. 'Things to Come' of 1935 used real people, a foreground model and the background reflected in a mirror close to the camera.

impression that one scene has dissolved into the other.

Fast and slow motion are achieved by running the film through the camera either slower or faster, respectively, than normal. Thus a film shot at 12 frames per second, when projected at 24 frames per second will be running at twice the shooting speed. True HIGH SPEED PHOTOGRAPHY requires specially designed cameras and shutters, and gives very much slowed down movements.

Other tricks can make use of the fact that a camera can make both near and distant objects appear in sharp focus, simply by using a small lens aperture. Thus a model dinosaur placed close to the camera can appear much larger than a human comparatively far away.

Effects departments

The idea of separate special effects departments began in Hollywood during the mid 1920s when the studios had grown so large that the various facets of movie making were being split up for the sake of efficiency. Before this it was the custom for the optical effects to be under the control of the cameraman, while the physical effects were handled by the prop men. The creation of separate effects departments meant that a reservoir of specialized knowledge was formed within each studio, with the result that the special effects in Hollywood-produced films reached a very high stan-

One of the most famous special effects films was 'King Kong', made in 1933, which was the origin of many effects techniques. There were six models of the whole Kong and a 20 foot (6.1 m) bust (left), covered with bear hides. In the well known scene below, actress Fay Wray was filmed being held by an 8 foot (2.4 m) mechanical arm, and this shot was then matted into a sequence made using the miniature Kong and pteranodon, frame by frame.

dard, particularly in the 1930s. In the 1960s, however, there was a trend away from studio production and many of the departments were forced to close down (this has also happened in Britain) and the older effects men were obliged to either retire or go freelance. Ironically, with the sudden popularity of the 'big disaster' type of film in the mid 1970s, such as *Earthquake*, the old techniques are once again in demand and many Hollywood effects experts have been brought out of retirement to work on them.

Optical effects Many of the optical effects used in the making of motion pictures were first invented by still photographers in the 19th century. One such technique is the *glass shot*, which is a painting on a sheet of glass positioned in front of the camera in such a way that it blends in with the real scene that the camera is photographing. Another early technique is the *matte shot*, one of the simplest ways of combining two image components on the same frame of film to create the illusion that they are part of the same scene. Basically it entails exposing only a portion of each frame of film, the unwanted part of the scene being obscured by a card cut to the required shape and placed in front of the camera lens. The card is called the *matte*. The film is then wound back and a new scene filmed, this time with the previously exposed portion of each frame

Below : travelling mattes are used where foreground action is to be shown against a moving background. Two complementary masked films are produced either by hand or mechanically and combined by an optical printer. One method uses a yellow, sodium-lit screen in front of which the action is played. A split prism camera splits the beam on to a normal film and a second, yellow-sensitive one recording the background and foreground separately.

obscured by another card—the *counter-matte*. The result is a *double exposure*. Silent film cameramen had a *matte box* attached to the front of their cameras which contained a number of differently shaped *mattes* with which they achieved many of the optical effects that are nowadays produced in the film laboratory with an optical printer (see MOVIE FILM PRODUCTION).

A variation of the *matte shot* is one that makes use of a *matte painting*. After filming a scene with the required portion matted out, the partially exposed film is then transferred to another camera, heavily weighted to prevent vibration, which is positioned in front of a sheet of black glass. An artist then paints, on to the glass, the desired image component that is to be added to the previously photographed scene (usually matte paintings are of background scenery, such as mountain ranges or city skylines). The painting is then filmed, with the black, unpainted section of the glass acting as a *counter-matte*. A later development of the *matte-shot* is the *travelling matte*, which is one that moves or changes its shape with each proceeding frame of film, such as when the foreground action is to be shown in movement across a moving background. One way to achieve this is to produce each individual matte and counter-matte by hand, a process similar to cartoon animation and just as time consuming. This method gives the best results (it was used in the making of *2001: A Space Odyssey*) but a number of quicker and cheaper photographic processes have been introduced, most of which make use of the various light-reacting layers of colour film to create 'automatic' mattes. One such process is called the *blue backing system*. In this the foreground action is lit with normal white light and is photographed on regular colour negative film against a blue background, either a blue-painted back cloth or a translucent blue screen lit from

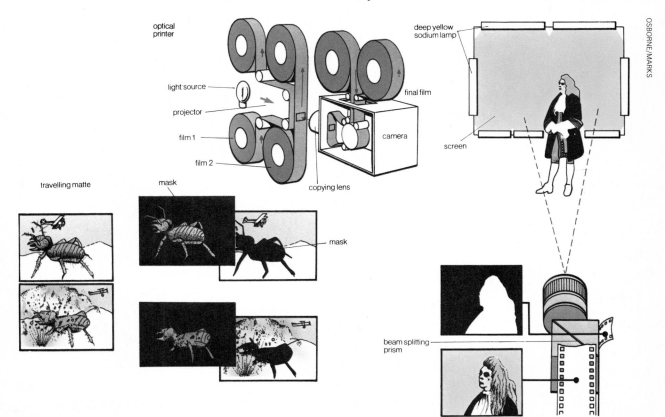

OSBORNE/MARKS

optical printer

light source

projector

film 1

film 2

copying lens

final film

camera

deep yellow sodium lamp

screen

travelling matte

mask

mask

beam splitting prism

behind. The colour and lighting level of the backing is such that it produces an exposure on only the blue sensitive layer of the colour negative to a density greater than that of any object in the foreground. A series of laboratory printing operations involving black and white litho film exposed through colour filters is then carried out to produce a foreground matte with an opaque area corresponding exactly to the image of the blue backing recorded on the colour negative. From this a *counter-matte* can be made in which the blue backing is shown as clear film with an opaque silhouette of the foreground action. The two image components are then combined, using the mattes, on to a duplicate negative in an optical printer.

Another method of combining separately filmed foreground and background action is called *rear* or *back projection*. For this the actors stand in front of a translucent screen on to which background action is projected from behind. The projector and the camera are synchronized so that as one frame of the background action is being projected the shutter of the camera is opening simultaneously. A later variation of this technique is *front projection*, in which the background is projected on to a particular type of screen in the same line of sight as the camera. This is done by means of a lightly silvered mirror at 45° just in front of the camera lens, which reflects the image from the projector on to the screen. Since the projector is in the same line of sight as the camera, no shadows are visible around the edges of the actors, and their bodies mask their shadows exactly. The REFLECTIVE MATERIAL on the screen consists of millions of tiny glass beads, each of which acts as an optically perfect reflex reflector. This system gives very high reflectivity in the direction of the projected beam, so that a comparatively low intensity beam can be used. In addition, although the background scene is also being projected on to the actors, their bodies are not highly reflective and they will not show the image.

Miniatures, or *models*, are traditionally included in the optical effects category. Miniature buildings or whole cities are often used in sequences in which widespread destruction is depicted (model buildings played an important part in such recent films as *Earthquake* and *The Towering Inferno*). War films often make use of miniature ships and aircraft (in *Tora! Tora! Tora!* both the Japanese and American fleets consisted entirely of models). Model ships used in films have varied in length from about 3 feet (90 cm) to over 50 feet (15 m). The latter are often actually filmed at sea, while the smaller versions are filmed on water tanks within the studio.

Mechanical effects

These can range from making a bullet hole appear in a wall to the blowing up of a whole building. The physical effects man has to be prepared to create whatever effects that the script writer includes in the screenplay. In recent years physical effects have involved mainly scenes of violence and destruction, such as simulated injuries, fires and explosions. The former category includes bullet hits, stabbings and spearings. Bullet hits are achieved by the actor wearing, beneath his clothes, a small explosive charge to which is often attached a plastic bag containing artificial blood. When the charge is detonated, either by the actor himself or by radio control, it blows a small hole in the clothing, as well as releasing the blood, creating the illusion that the actor has been shot. Stabbings are simulated by the use of knives made of resin and coated with metallic paint. Artificial blood, contained in the handle, can be squeezed out through small vents in the blade. Spears and arrows fly to their targets guided by fine wires attached to cork-covered metal plates worn by the

Above left, and above: many films require the destruction of cities on a large scale, but the models required for these can be quite small. These models were made for a BBC film of Tolstoy's 'War and Peace', and represent the burning of Moscow. Although when viewed along the line of sight of the camera it appears as if there are a large number of houses, as above, in reality there are only a few models as the shot on its left reveals.

Left: another way of producing an 'instant Moscow'. Here a glass artist paints a skyline that will eventually appear to merge into a foreground field, actually in Yugoslavia. Assembled armies and a river can also be painted directly on to the real landscape as seen from a particular viewpoint through the glass. The depth of focus of the camera ensures that everything is in sharp focus.

Below: one of the most successful effects films of recent years was '2001: A Space Odyssey'. In one scene, an actor moves weightlessly through the brain centre of a giant computer. This seemingly horizontal shot was actually taken looking upwards, the set being three storeys high. The actor was suspended by wires from the roof.

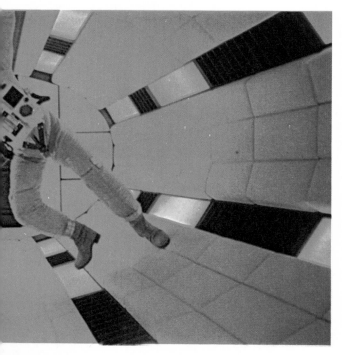

actors. The spears or arrows, which are hollow, are propelled along the wires by pneumatic devices off-camera.

Full scale explosions and fires represent the more spectacular work of the physical effects men, who must be fully qualified explosive experts. In Hollywood they are required to take a State approved course in explosives and pass an examination. In Britain the restrictions on explosives are even more severe, and even the small charges used for bullet hits can only be obtained by effects men who are approved by the Home Office and hold police certificates. Fire effects can be just as dangerous, especially if they involve the simulation of people burning. The safest method of achieving the latter effect involves the use of a small gas burner that an actor can wear under fire-proofed clothing. When the gas is ignited it appears that a portion of the actor's clothing is alight but the flames will vanish as soon as the supply of gas is switched off. Another method is for a stunt man to wear protective clothing that has been smeared with alcohol. When ignited the burning alcohol creates a vapour barrier between the flames and the clothing. For a stunt man to be completely enveloped in flames he must wear a heavily insulated asbestos suit which contains its own air supply.

To create the illusion that buildings are on fire, effects men have developed a portable unit that consists of a motor and a modified pump capable of pumping paraffin [kerosene] from ground level to burners situated up to 100 feet (30 m) above the unit. A number of burners, placed at open windows and on the roof of a building, can turn it into a raging inferno when the unit is activated, but the building actually remains untouched. Effects men prefer to use paraffin for fire scenes because it is more economical than oil or petrol [gasoline] and there is much less likelihood of any spilt fuel igniting. Colouring agents are usually added to the fuel mixture as 'real' flames are apt to appear transparent on film.

Model animation

This specialized form of special effects, like most effects techniques, dates back to the earliest days of the cinema. One of the first films to feature the process was made in 1897 by the Vitagraph company in America. Called *Humpty Dumpty Circus*, it used animated wooden toy animals, and in 1907 film pioneer Edwin S Porter spent twelve hours a day for a week animating seven small teddy bears. The resulting film, called *The Teddy Bears*, lasted only a few minutes but was a big success at the time. Model animation is achieved through *stop-motion photography*. This involves positioning the model by hand for each separate frame of film. For one second of movement on the screen the model must be adjusted and photographed 24 times (film cameras and projectors run at 24 frames per second), which is why the process is a lengthy and time consuming one. The most famous name in the field is that of Willis H O'Brien who, in films like *The Lost World* and *King Kong*, was the first to combine model animation with live action. This is mostly achieved by a system called *miniature projection*, a smaller version of rear projection. In miniature screen work a scaled set containing the models is set up in front of the screen, then a single frame of the live action is projected on to the screen as the models are photographed. The models are then adjusted, the next frame of the live action appears on the screen behind them and the two image components are again photographed together. When skilfully executed both models and live action integrate perfectly in the completed film, creating such illusions as a man being pursued by a giant dinosaur which is, in reality, a model only a few inches tall.

SPECIFIC GRAVITY and vapour density

In everyday life the word 'heaviness' is often not used in its strictly correct meaning of referring to the weights of objects; for example gold is thought of as being a 'heavier' metal than aluminium, even though an aluminium saucepan weighs more than a gold ring. The important idea here is that *equal volumes* of the two materials should be weighed. The MASS of a standard volume of a substance is called its *density*, and the actual value of the density depends on the units in which the mass and volume are measured. The density of iron, for example, is 7.9 grammes per cubic centimetre (in the metric system), or 494 pounds per cubic foot (in the British system). An alternative way of measuring density is to compare the mass of a certain volume of the substance with the same volume of water. This type of density measurement is known as the *specific gravity* (or *relative density*) of the object, and it is a dimensionless number (see DIMENSIONS) because it is the ratio of two masses. The specific gravity of iron is 7.9; and it is worth noting that specific gravity is always numerically the same as the density in grammes per cubic centimetre, because the density of water is very close to 1 g/cm³.

The practical uses of measuring specific gravity were first demonstrated by ARCHIMEDES of Syracuse (in Sicily) in the 3rd century BC, when, according to legend, he was consulted by Hiero, the ruler of Syracuse, as to how it would be possible to detect whether the gold in a crown had been alloyed with silver by the goldsmith. The story goes that Archimedes hit on the answer when about to take a bath, and ran home through the streets of Syracuse, shouting 'Eureka' ('I have found it'). He realized that when he immersed himself in the bath the volume of water which overflowed was equal to the volume of body immersed; and hence that if equal weights of silver and gold were immersed the more dense gold would displace less water. He then showed that the crown displaced more water than an equal weight of gold, so proving that the forgery had taken place.

Measuring the SG of liquids

Archimedes also realized that when an object is immersed in liquid, the liquid surrounding it must be exerting an upward force (the *buoyancy force*) which would just support the same volume of liquid if the body were not there. The object must thus experience an *upthrust* equal to the weight of liquid displaced by it; this is the usual statement of *Archimedes' principle*. For a body which is more dense than the liquid, the buoyancy force is less than its weight, so it sinks; but a less dense body will only sink into the liquid until it has displaced a sufficient volume of liquid for the buoyancy force to be equal to its weight, and it will then float with part of its volume out of the liquid. This is the principle of the *hydrometer*, an instrument for measuring the specific gravities of liquids. In its simplest form it is just a float made of a glass bulb weighted with lead shot, with a long narrow neck which rises above the surface of the liquid. When the hydrometer is floated in different liquids it must always displace the same *weight* of liquid (equal to its own weight), so the *volume* displaced depends on the specific gravity of the liquid. The level of the liquid surface at the neck of the hydro-

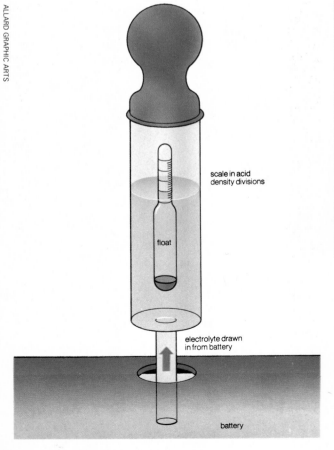

scale in acid density divisions

float

electrolyte drawn in from battery

battery

Above: a well known example of the effect of different specific gravities. Ice has a slightly lower specific gravity (0.92) than water, so an iceberg just manages to float.

Right: the pousse café, a cocktail, makes use of the different specific gravities of, from the bottom, crème de cacao, maraschino, yellow Chartreuse, Bénédictine, green Chartreuse and brandy.

Left: the principle of the hydrometer, for measuring the specific gravity of liquids, is that a body will float at different heights depending on the specific gravity of the liquid. There is no room inside a battery for a float, so a hydrometer consists of a tube with a rubber bulb, enabling a sample of the liquid to be drawn in.

meter indicates the depth at which it floats, and as this depends on the volume of liquid displaced, it is possible to graduate the neck in terms of the specific gravity of the liquid.

In a practical hydrometer the float is usually in a glass container which is filled with liquid by suction, using a rubber bulb, as it is then easier to see the liquid level and less liquid is needed. Probably the best known use is for measuring the state of lead-acid batteries, in which the liquid (electrolyte) has a specific gravity of 1.28 when fully charged, but this decreases as the battery is discharged. Hydrometers are also used for measuring the proof of spirits, and for following the fermentation of liquors, whose specific gravity falls as the sugar in solution is converted to alcohol.

Vapour density The density of gases and vapours is about a thousand times less than that of solids and liquids, so correspondingly accurate techniques are required to measure it. The measurement of these *vapour densities* of substances which are normally liquid (at room temperature and pressure) has been particularly important in chemistry, as it is related to the molecular weight of the substance. One accurate method is to balance two evacuated containers in an atmosphere of the vapour, and then to puncture one, so that buoyancy forces no longer act on it. The upthrust on the other is equal to the weight of vapour now in the punctured container, and so, from this force and the volume of the first container, the density of the vapour can be calculated.

SPECIFIC HEAT (see calorimetry)

SPECTACLES

It is not known with certainty who was the inventor of spectacles, and it was not until the end of the 13th century that any documentary reference to them can be found. The English monk Roger BACON and the Italian Allesandro della Spina are among the many who are claimed to have discovered spectacles. The first portrait of a man wearing spectacles was a fresco painted in 1352 by Tommaso da Modena.

By the 15th century, spectacle making was well established in Europe, and when the printing press was invented there was a resulting upsurge in the demand for spectacles. It must be remembered, however, that only convex LENSES were made at first, which would have been of use in cases of *hypermetropia* (long sightedness) and *presbyopia* (long sightedness caused by loss of accommodation in the eye) but not *myopia* (short sightedness). Spectacles with concave lenses to correct myopia were not available until the beginning of the 16th century, Pope Leo X was one of the first to wear them.

Frame materials The very earliest spectacles had lenses mounted in heavy circular frames of copper, lead or wood. Later, leather, bone and horn were used, and by the early 17th century light frames of steel were being manufactured. In the 18th century tortoiseshell joined the list of frame materials and spectacles assumed the basic design we know today.

Below: a portrait of Pope Leo X painted by Raphael in about 1517. Leo X, here seen holding a reading glass, was one of the first people to make use of concave lenses for correcting myopia.

Nowadays, spectacle frames are generally made of metal or plastic. The most commonly used plastics are cellulose acetate, cellulose nitrate and the acrylic resins, which are *thermoplastics*, that is to say they soften on heating and harden again when cooled. Cellulose acetate discolours less than cellulose nitrate, it is not flammable, can be worked easily and is fairly long lasting. Cellulose nitrate, however, although it tends to discolour and is flammable, is more rigid and keeps its shape well. Acrylic resins such as 'Perspex' ['Plexiglas'] are not affected by body acids and can be more brilliantly coloured than the cellulose plastics, but they are more difficult to manipulate.

One of the most popular metal framing materials is 'rolled gold', which has a core made of a base metal such as brass covered with a cladding of gold. Stainless steel, anodized aluminium, nickel silver and gold plated and rhodium plated metals are also used.

Cellulose acetate for spectacle frames is prepared by stacking thin sheets of differently coloured cellulose acetate, applying a solvent and a plasticizer, and subjecting the stack to hydraulic pressure to produce a homogeneous mass from the pile. This compacted pile of sheets is then turned over on its side and sliced into sheets from three to six mm (0.12 to 0.24 inch) thick. The direction of the cut is at right angles to the plane of the original sheet and this gives rise to the characteristic mottling of the material (often called *sliced acetate*).

Extruded cellulose acetate is much harder than sliced acetate, it has a longer life and accepts a finer polish. It is made by heating cellulose acetate granules with a suitable plasticizer in a cylinder, and then forcing the plastic material under high pressure through a slot whose dimensions determine the size of the finished sheet (see EXTRUSION). Colour effects are produced by squeezing materials of different colours into the slot.

Frame construction Frames today are virtually all mass produced, and about 100 separate operations are carried out on each frame made. The fronts of plastic frames are made on a *routing machine*. Slabs of material are bolted to formers and the eyepiece holes are routed out by small vertical milling tools. Grooves are then cut in the rims to accept the lenses. The *bridge* is formed by shaping the frame after it has been softened by heating. The sidepieces are produced by injection or compression moulding and the reinforcing wires are inserted either during moulding or subsequently with heating. Before assembly, the frame components are polished in rotating barrels containing pumice balls. Assembly is done on a specially designed jig, the metal joints being pinned right through or pressed in under heat.

Metal frames are usually worked by coining, striking, crimping and bending. These operations cause the metal to become very hard, and to bring it back to a workable condition it has to be *annealed*. In this operation the frames are coated with a protective solution and then heated to a high temperature in an electric furnace. The frames are removed, cooled in water and cleaned. The parts are assembled by electrical *spot welding*, and finally plastic nose pads and side tips are added.

Lenses The GLASS normally used for spectacle lenses is *spectacle crown*, which has a *refractive index* (a measure of the ability of an optical material to bend light) of 1.523, although a glass has been developed recently with a refractive index of 1.70, which is lighter and thinner than crown glass of the same power. For large eyesize frames the lenses are often made of acrylic plastics which are much lighter than glass. Glass and plastics for spectacle lenses must be homogeneous, free of *striae* (linear faults), bubbles, milkiness or strain (see OPTICS

JOHN WATNEY

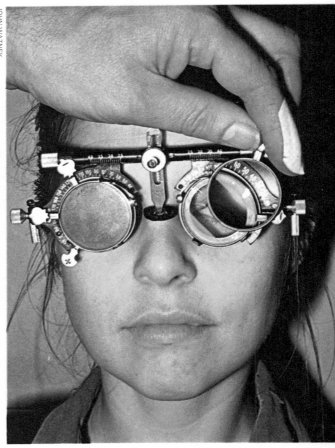

Left : a spectacle pedlar in the 16th century. In those days spectacles were not made to prescription and were simply selected by trial and error.

Below left : an optician will sometimes use a trial frame like this one to hold lenses in front of the patient's eyes. The trial frame is graduated so that the dimensions of the frame to be prescribed can be determined and also so that the optician will know the orientation of the test lenses (important if they are toric).

Below : a refractor head serves the same purpose as a trial frame, but the test lenses are selected automatically.

Below right : plastic spectacle frames are made on a routing machine. Here, the operator mills the outer rim of a frame to the approximate final shape.

PRODUCTION). The power of ophthalmic lenses, as with other lenses, is expressed in *dioptres* which is the reciprocal of the focal length in metres.

Spectacle lenses are produced in *meniscus* (one surface convex, the other concave), *spherical* or *toric* form. Toric lenses have surfaces with a different curvature in one plane from that in a plane at right angles ; they are used to correct *astigmatism* which is caused by uneven curvature of the surface of the eye. Simple spherical lenses are used to correct near sightedness and far sightedness. Tinted lenses are produced by colouring the glass batch or by vacuum coating the finished lenses with metal oxides. *Photochromic* glass which darkens or lightens according to the light intensity is made by including silver halides in the glass composition. Safety glasses for industrial wear are made of laminated glass, toughened glass or plastics.

Multifocal lenses are commonly employed nowadays where more than one vision defect has to be corrected. *Bifocal* lenses for example have an upper section for distant vision and a smaller lower section for near vision or reading. There are two types of bifocal lenses, *one piece bifocals* and *fused bifocals*. The former, invented about the beginning of the century, are made by polishing two differently shaped surfaces on to one side of the lens. With fused bifocals, a small spherical indentation is polished on to the outer convex surface of the main lens to accept a small lens which will form the reading section of the finished bifocal. The small lens is placed in position and the assembly heated in a furnace until the two sections fuse together. To provide the higher power needed for read-

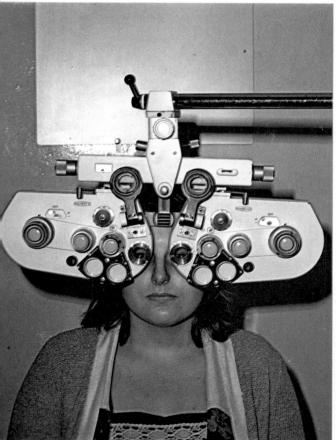

ing, the small lens which forms the reading section is made of glass having a higher refractive index than the main lens.

Sight testing   Before a pair of spectacles can be made up, the patient's sight must be tested by an optician to determine what type of lenses are needed and what power is required. This can be done by objective or subjective tests, but preferably both.

The dioptric power of the eye can be measured with an *optometer*. This projects a *collimated* (parallel) beam of light from an illuminated target on to the reflective layer of the retina at the back of the eye. The collimated beam is adjusted to obtain a sharp retinal image as viewed through an eyepiece by the optician. The power of the eye lens can then be read off from a linear scale on the instrument. The instrument can be rotated to measure errors in the two principal planes. A recently developed instrument is the *ophthalmetron* which electronically scans the retina and records on a print-out the power in every plane.

The refractive condition of the eye can also be tested with a *retinoscope*. This consists of a light source, a movable condensing lens to adjust the convergence or divergence of the beam which is situated between the light source and a split mirror or a mirror with a central aperture. The patient 'fixes' a distant object and the optician directs the light beam into the patient's eye with the mirror. The light is reflected from the retinal layer and appears as a red reflection in the patient's pupil. The observation of the reflection by the optician through the sight hole in the mirror, and its movement with respect to the movement of the retinoscope, shows the refractive condition of the eye. In myopia there is a movement of the reflection in the same direction as the retinoscope light beam. In hypermetropia (often called *hyperopia*) the reflection moves in the opposite direction. A scissors-like movement demonstrates that there is some astigmatism present. The OPHTHALMOSCOPE,

a device used by doctors to examine the interior of the eye, works on a similar principle.

Once the sight defect has been diagnosed, trial lenses are placed before the patient's eye until the movement of the reflected beam observed with the retinoscope is no longer apparent. The particular combination of lenses needed will tell the optician what prescription is required for the spectacle lenses. The trial lenses accept the selected lenses, or they may be automatically selected in a *refractor head*, an independently supported instrument which can be positioned in front of the patient's eyes.

In a typical subjective sight test, the patient views a test chart at a distance of six metres (20 feet). One eye is covered and spherical lenses are placed in front of the other eye progressively until the sharpest acuity of the characters is obtained. The cylindrical lenses are added if astigmatism is found to be present. There are various techniques for determining the type of spherical and cylindrical components necessary in the spectacles, for example the use of a *block and fan* chart and a *crossed cylinder* method of finding the axis and power of any cylinder correction that may be required. After carrying out the procedure for one eye, it is then repeated for both eyes.

In the UK prescriptions for spectacles are made up at *prescription houses* which keep stocks of all types of lenses both finished and semi-finished, frames, frame parts and other optical equipment. Before being inserted into a frame, each lens must be 'marked up' on an optical marking device called a *focimeter*, then cut to size and shape on a semi or fully automatic edging machine. For this operation the lens is held between felt pads on a spindle and is rotated slowly against high speed diamond wheels which also provide the 'V' edge necessary on the finished lens.

SPECTROPHOTOMETER (see spectroscope)

Above: the shape of the bridge of a pair of spectacles is altered by means of a specially designed hand tool.

Right: this chart is used in making up spectacles. It enables the technician to be sure that the axes of any cylindrical elements in the lens prescription are correctly oriented in the frames. Astigmatism is corrected with lenses of this sort.

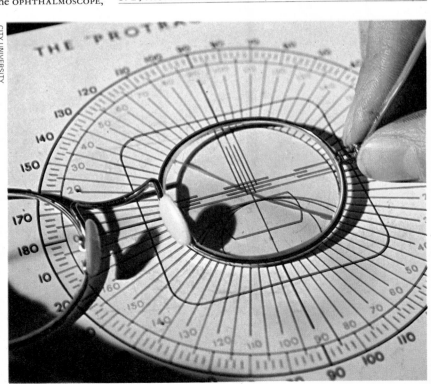

SPECTROSCOPE and spectrometer

In its simplest form, a spectroscope is a device for observing the spectrum of colours produced by a PRISM or a DIFFRACTION GRATING. This is now rarely done except in teaching, but the basic technique has led to a wide variety of devices such as the spectrograph, the spectrometer, the spectrophotometer and the colorimeter.

In spectroscopes and spectrographs the whole spectrum of light radiation is observed at once by eye or on a photograph. Spectrometers, on the other hand, usually select one particular small group of wavelengths for measurement by, for example, a photocell, and usually there is some way of scanning this 'window' of wavelengths over a larger range. There are both *emission* and *absorption* spectra to be studied: emission spectra consist of a series of bright individual colours, while absorption spectra are seen against the complete spectrum of colour and look as if individual colours are missing.

Spectroscopes The design of the elementary spectroscope, as found in schools, has changed little since the 18th century. White light is passed through a *collimator* consisting of a slit and a lens to define a narrow beam of parallel light, and is then split up with respect to wavelength by either a prism or a diffraction grating. The resulting spectrum is then examined by means of a small telescope which is focused on the distance of the slit. If the prism were not there and the telescope looked straight at the slit, it would show a sharp image of the slit. When the prism is put in place, the beam is deviated through an angle depending on the wavelengths, so that there is now no longer a single slit image, but one for each colour. The resolution depends upon the width of the slit, and this can usually be varied. For a source consisting of all colours, such as an ordinary electric light, the result is a complete and continuous spectrum.

Often the prism or grating is placed at the centre of a small circular table graduated in degrees round which the telescope and the collimator can be moved on a common centre. If·the dispersion of the spectrum is high, the telescope will have to be moved round to examine various parts of it.

A laboratory version of this, known as a wavelength spectrometer, has a fixed collimator and telescope and a *constant deviation prism* shaped so that the angle between the collimated beam and the deviated beam is always a right angle. By rotating the prism, different wavelengths can be sent to the telescope, and the prism's rotating drum can be calibrated directly in wavelength.

Wavelengths can be measured either in nanometres—thousand millionths of a metre—or in angstroms, a more traditional unit. Yellow light has a wavelength of about 550 nm or 5500 angstroms. At infra-red wavelengths it is more usual to talk in terms of *wavenumbers*: the reciprocal of the wavelength in centimetres. A wavenumber of 4000 is therefore 2.5 microns or 2500 nm.

Spectrographs By replacing the human eye with a photographic plate or film, a permanent record of the spectrum is obtained. This can then be measured on a *densitometer* to give a graph of the spectrum, in which case the 'lines' observed with the eye, in effect each one being an image of the slit, are represented as peaks (for emission lines) or dips (for absorption lines) on the graph. A photographic spectroscope is

Below left: a typical 19th century spectroscope, viewing a burner spectrum. The nearer telescope contains a scale, illuminated by a candle, which is reflected into the field of view by the prism face.

Below: the acetylene flame of an atomic absorption spectrophotometer vaporizes the sample, and the emission spectrum of the element being measured is then shone through the flame. A monochromator isolates one line, so that any absorption due to that element is revealed.

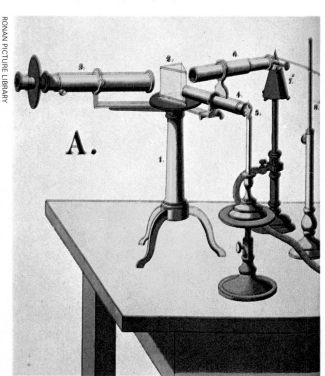

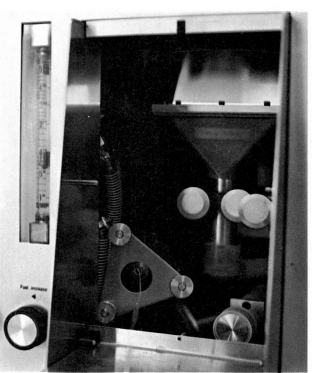

FORD DUNTON EXHAUST EMISSION LAB

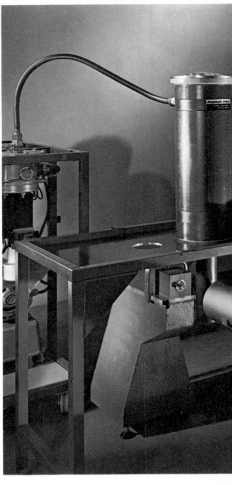

Three widely different uses of spectrometers. Above: an infra-red gas analyzer, here measuring the exhaust of a car, is helping to reduce atmospheric pollution; centre, a Mössbauer spectrometer in an atomic energy establishment, an advanced piece of equipment which depends on nuclear absorption and emission of gamma rays at very low temperatures. The resonant frequencies of atomic nuclei can be measured with great precision with this apparatus; far right, this borehole logger is completely transportable yet can measure small concentrations of tin within 30 seconds by X-ray fluorescence.

known as a spectrograph, and the photographs it takes are strictly called *spectrograms*, though in practice they are often just called 'spectra'. Spectrographs were attached to telescopes in the 19th century in order to produce stellar spectra; the technique was applied to industry in about 1908, in which case the sample to be analyzed formed one of a pair of electrodes across which a current was passed, forming an arc as in an ARC LAMP.

Modern spectrographs for spectrochemical analysis do not record the whole spectrum where they have a specific job to do. Instead, the *direct reading* technique will be used: a series of PHOTOMULTIPLIER TUBES or light detectors are set up, each one dedicated to measuring the intensity of a separate spectrum line.

Absorption systems Initially, as with emission spectroscopy, work in this field was limited to the visible region of

the spectrum. Early instruments employed a series of coloured optical FILTERS to isolate the chosen part of the spectrum in what was called an *absorptiometer* or *colorimeter*. The sample, in liquid form, was placed in a *cuvette* with transparent parallel faces through which the light passed before reaching a photo-cell detector. Sometimes two detectors were used in parallel to give a steadier reading. Absorption of light by the sample (*absorbance*) was measured and compared with that of known standards to establish the concentration.

Although still used where low resolution work is adequate, these filter instruments are limited and have largely been replaced by those using *monochromators*.

A monochromator is a device which isolates specific small groups of wavelengths using either a prism or a diffraction grating. Gratings have the advantage that they spread the spectrum out evenly over the wavelengths, while prisms bunch up the wavelengths at the red end. In addition, by giving the grating a reflective coating, it will perform at all wavelengths since all colours are reflected equally well, within the limitations of the type of coating and the spacing of the grating lines. Prisms can be made of materials such as quartz or sodium chloride (rock salt) to transmit infra-red or ultra-violet, however.

By mechanically rotating the grating or prism, as in the spectroscope, a beam of any chosen colour, just a few angstroms wide, can be isolated: a second slit selects only those

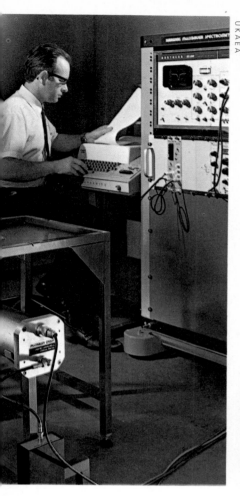

wavelengths required. The *bandwidth*—the range of wavelengths transmitted—can be varied by altering the slit width in order to pass more light at lower resolution if necessary. The monochromator replaces the filters of the simpler instruments.

Spectrophotometers

A *photometer* is a device which measures light intensity, so a spectrophotometer is the strictly accurate word for a device which measures the distribution of light over a spectrum. An elementary spectrophotometer consists of a monochromator with a light source chosen for the spectral range of interest, a sample compartment, a detector and a readout system. Measurements are carried out at one wavelength at a time, and wavelengths are changed manually.

The way in which the recording versions of spectrophotometers work—that is, in which the spectrum is scanned by the machine automatically and a graph drawn of the absorption—varies with the wavelength being used. In both infrared and ultra-violet cases the sample under examination is compared with a reference sample: for example, if the concentration of a water soluble dye is to be measured, the reference would consist of pure water. In the infra-red system, the beam from the light source is split into two beams, one for the reference and one for the sample. The beams are then recombined by a chopping mechanism so that first one beam, then the other is sent through the monochromator in rapid succession. The detector then records the light variations. If there

is no difference between the reference and sample at a particular wavenumber, there will be no output from the detector. If, however, there is a difference, then the detector will record an oscillating (that is, alternating current) output which can be registered by a PEN RECORDER.

In the ultra-violet and visible versions, scattering of light by the system is a great problem and the samples have to be placed as close to the detector as possible. In this case the monochromator comes first, then the beams are split. A common method of recording is to use a glass density wedge in one beam, which is moved up and down to equalize the intensities recorded by the detector. The movement of this wedge is coupled to the pen: a similar system is used in the scanning microdensitometer illustrated on page 720 of *How it Works*.

Infra-red scanning spectrophotometers are widely used in chemical ANALYSIS and in gas analysis. The ultra-violet and visible versions tend to be used more for determining concentrations of absorbing materials, and in many cases do not scan but operate at fixed wavelengths. Hospitals, for example, use *auto-analyzers* which measure concentrations in a wide variety of fluids.

The *atomic absorption* spectrophotometer has a flame into which the sample is sprayed. Absorption takes place, providing a precise measure of very low concentrations of elements—less than one part per million.

SPECTROSCOPY

Spectroscopy is the analysis of light, or other forms of radiation, in terms of its *spectrum*. Its importance lies in the fact that all materials have a characteristic 'signature' of wavelengths in the spectrum: this results in *spectrochemical analysis*, for example, in order to find out what materials are in a given sample for laboratory purposes, and in astronomical spectroscopy, by means of which many apparently unattainable details of stars and galaxies have been discovered.

A spectrum (plural *spectra*) is the arrangement of waves in order of their wavelength (see WAVE MOTION). Light wavelengths are just part of the entire spectrum of ELECTROMAGNETIC RADIATION, which ranges from the very long wavelengths of radio to the very short gamma rays. On either side of the visible region are the infra-red (longer wavelengths) and ultra-violet (shorter). The spectrum can also be thought of in terms of the QUANTUM THEORY, in which a quantum of, say, blue light has greater energy than one of red light.

Early spectroscopy

Even in his first experiments with a PRISM in about 1665, NEWTON noticed that in the spectrum of sunlight there are a number of fine dark lines superimposed on the bright rainbow of colours, which he took to be boundaries between colours. At the beginning of the 19th century, Fraunhofer found that there are a large number of these lines, and he catalogued several hundred of them though their cause was unknown. It was not until the work of KIRCHHOFF and Bunsen that the true nature of the Fraunhofer lines was realized. Each line corresponds to the bright line that would be produced by an element glowing, such as when burnt in a flame, and so provides a means of identifying that element.

Spectrum theory

After half a century of listing and charting the lines of the spectra of the elements in the laboratory, mathematically trained physicists began to realize not only why some spectra are simple and some complicated, but also to recognize the changes in each kind of atom which produce each line. This kind of work is called the *theory of spectra* or spectrum theory, so as not to confuse it with spectrochemical analysis, and has led to new knowledge of ATOMS and ISOTOPES in particular. It depends very heavily on the acceptance of the quantum theory, which maintains that energy is not continuous, but is always produced in discrete 'packets' called *quanta* (the plural of quantum). A spectral line is produced and radiated when an electron moves from one orbital or energy level around the atom's nucleus to another nearer the nucleus. A change from a nearer orbital to a further one, caused by the addition of energy, results in absorption of the energy and hence an absorption line or possibly fluorescence if the energy is reradiated at another wavelength.

In the 'planetary' model of the atom due to Niels BOHR, one imagines the electrons as if they were planets orbiting the central nucleus in well defined orbits. Later work showed up discrepancies in this picture, and nowadays one thinks in terms of an 'orbital'—a region where the electron has the highest probability of being. Nevertheless, the concept of orbits of definite sizes is good enough for descriptive purposes.

Since each element has atoms which are different from every other element by virtue of their different number of nuclear particles, each spectral line is unique to a particular element. For example, an atom of helium has two protons and two neutrons in its nucleus, whereas hydrogen has only one of each. The greater charge on the nucleus resulting from the two protons produces orbitals which are of smaller radius than those of hydrogen. The energy, and hence wavelength,

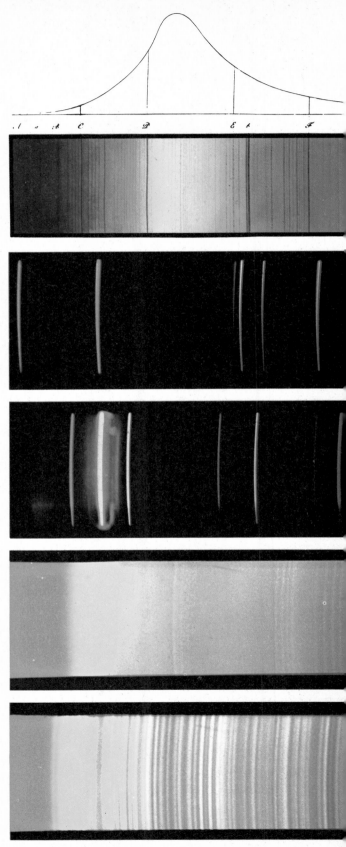

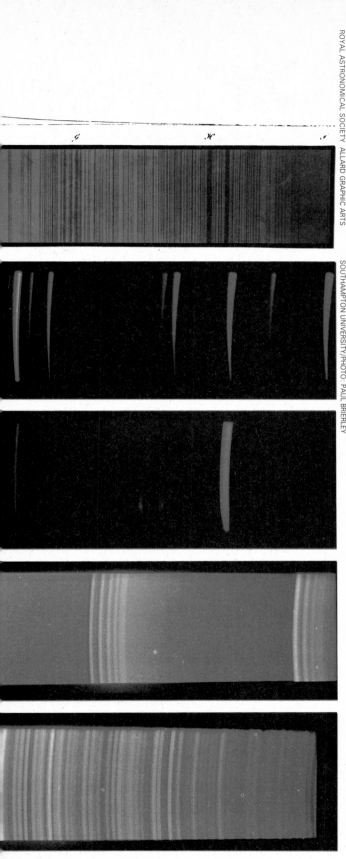

Various types of spectrum. Top, Fraunhofer's labelling of the absorption lines in the Sun's spectrum—C, F and G are the Balmer series of hydrogen. Above it is a graph of the light distribution, made with a prism, which compresses the red end. Lockyer discovered the element helium by its solar absorption lines: its emission spectrum is shown next. Sodium has two bright orange 'D' lines close together, responsible for the characteristic colour of streetlights. The spectrum of a carbon arc in air, second from bottom, shows the bands typical of molecular spectra, as the molecule CN, cyanogen, is formed. At bottom, iron's emission spectrum has many lines.

depends in part on the radii of the orbitals involved, so the wavelength of radiation emitted by an electron jumping from the second to the first orbital of helium is shorter than that emitted by an electron jumping between the same two orbitals of hydrogen. But larger atoms of heavier elements have orbitals which are much further out than the lowest ones of hydrogen, so they can produce radiation of longer wavelengths.

A gas at low pressure produces its characteristic glowing *emission* lines by the process just described. But in the case of an incandescent solid, the radiation emitted is not in discrete individual lines but is continuous—a continuum of *black body* radiation (see ELECTROMAGNETIC RADIATION). This gives rise to the complete rainbow of colour. In the case of the Sun, this continuum is crossed by the dark *absorption* lines which are due to cool gases in the Sun's outer atmosphere. Light coming from the Sun may be absorbed by an atom at its characteristic wavelength—the wavelength at which it glows. There is no reason why the atom should retain this energy, and it immediately reradiates it at the same frequency, but the chance of it travelling in the original direction is small. The effect on the observer is that the radiation at that particular frequency has been absorbed, producing a dark line at that part of the spectrum compared with the bright continuum.

While atoms give rise to individual line spectra, molecules or groups of atoms usually produce wider band spectra. These are particularly important in *spectrophotometry*, in which fairly low quality graphs of spectra are produced by machine (see SPECTROSCOPE).

Spectrochemical analysis One early spectroscopist was Norman Lockyer, an amateur astronomer working as a clerk at the War Office in London, who went on to become one of the most famous scientists of the 19th century. To study spectra in the laboratory, he applied a high current to two *poles* of metal, producing a glowing spark as in an ARC LAMP, and photographed the resulting spectrum to give a pattern of lines in which the strongest were also the longest. He was able to measure the intensity of a line by its length, and, working on gold alloys from the Royal Mint, he found an error made by a chemist in one of the standard alloys provided for him to test.

Wheatstone, one of the first electrical engineers, tried to use a spectroscope to prove that the electricity from a battery was the same kind of thing as electricity from a sparking coil; he used a spectroscope to examine the arc from two pieces of each of the metals copper, zinc, lead and tin, and published an approximate diagram of the spectra, but he had no way of measuring wavelengths. He forecast that this might one day become a method of analyzing metals, and this technique forms the basis of modern spectrochemical analysis.

Spectrographs were first used in metallurgical laboratories in the years 1915 to 1935. The first methods used involved photographing the spectra, then examining the plates by eye

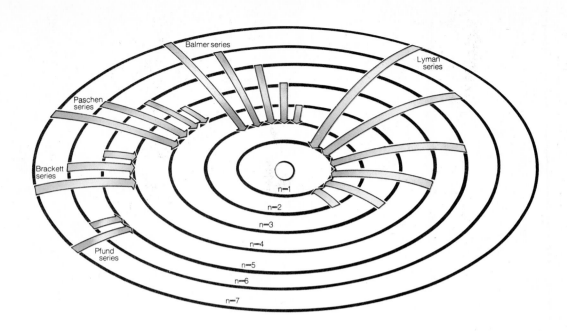

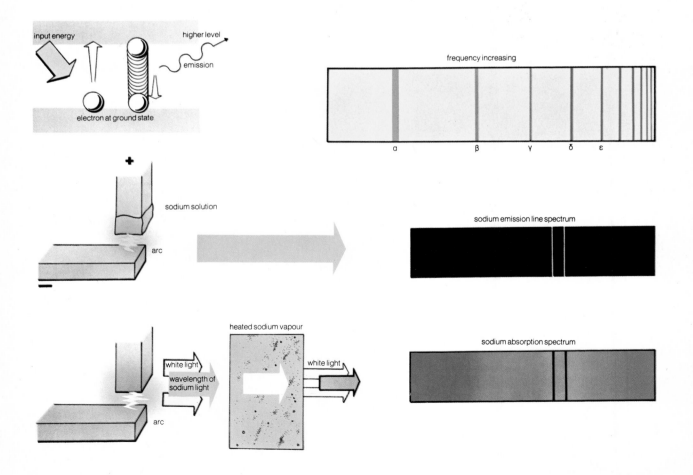

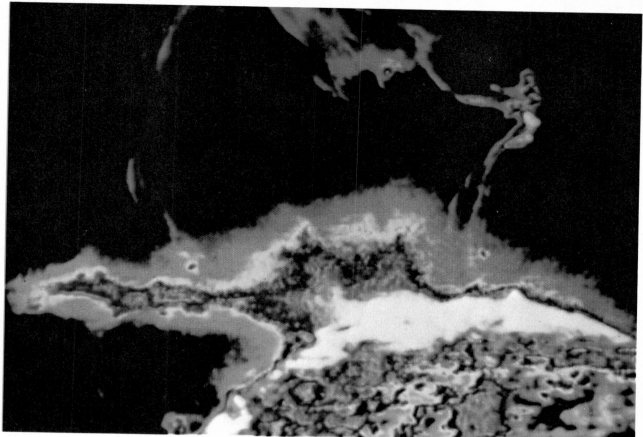

By viewing the Sun in one isolated wavelength of light, here an ultra-violet helium line, seen from Skylab, features not visible in white light are seen. The colours represent varying intensities.

Left: at top is a schematic view of an atom, with the orbitals shown as circular orbits. In the case of hydrogen, there is just one electron. Jumps down to the ground state, where n = 1, produce the Lyman series of spectral lines, in the ultra-violet: Lyman α is at 122 nm. Shown below this is the Balmer series, best known because it appears in the visible region of the spectrum with hydrogen α at 656 nm. The production of emission and absorption lines of sodium is also shown, emission from a sodium arc and absorption seen when white light from an arc is passed through sodium vapour.

or, later, on a photographic measuring device such as a DENSITO-METER. In the 1930s the direct spectrometer came into use, which scanned the spectrum directly by means of a photocell, giving a reading on a meter or drawing a graph. During World War 2, spectrochemical analysis became one of the main quality control methods used by suppliers of alloys of alumin-ium, magnesium, copper, lead and steel throughout the world. Now equipment has been so far automated that a direct reading spectrometer will compare the composition of a sample with a standard alloy, and print out the results on the lineprinter output from a computer which has made any comparison or corrections needed for the test; the whole operation can be carried out in five minutes. In a foundry this has the result that a batch of molten metal can be analyzed, and the result sent to the foundry foreman, so quickly as to provide analytical

control for each batch of metal without keeping it hot at great expense of power while awaiting analysis by a slower method.

An equally quick and basic application of spectrochemical analysis is by the use of X-ray fluorescence, both in mining, and in examining alloys for quality control. In this case, a sample 'illuminated' with X-rays fluoresces at certain wave-lengths, in a similar way to the production of absorption lines. The sample can be any powdered material, or a solid disc of metal, and this kind of apparatus too has been automated so as to supply six to twenty analytical results for a single sample within ten minutes. For X-rays it is convenient to think of the radiation as particles, rather than as waves, and to count the particles with a PHOTOMULTIPLIER TUBE: again the results can be printed out automatically.

For mineral prospecting, portable fluorescence equipment has been made which uses a radioactive isotope instead of a high voltage generator to provide the power. The radiation from the isotope emerges from a window in the surface of the machine which is applied to the surface of the mineral in a mine. Only one element is detected and analyzed at a time, but by interchangeable filters the same equipment can be used for several metals. This method only differs from the X-ray spectrochemical analyzer in that using an isotope to emit GAMMA RAYS is more efficient, in terms of weight of equipment, than using X-rays of rather longer wavelength.

X-ray fluorescence analysis is also replacing other spectro-chemical methods in museum laboratories, where it has the advantage that one can analyze an object without damaging it; this method can be used for such various specimens as the glaze on pottery, the paints of an antique painting, or the precious metal plating on an object made of a cheaper metal.

Forensic laboratories take advantage of the very small samples needed for analysis, such as paint flakes from the clothes of the victim of a car accident.

Perhaps the most important applications of spectrochemical analysis are its medical uses in the testing of samples of any liquid in the body, of meat and plants, and of the impurities which pollute the air we breathe and the water we drink. This application began with the detection of poisons in the digestive system, whether due to chronic or sudden poisoning where only a few parts in a million of an element as lead or mercury may be dangerous. Then it spread to routine tests of any element normally found in blood serum and other liquids, but gradually spectrophotometry took over this kind of work from ordinary spectrochemical analysis. A few years ago there was a widespread outbreak of mercury poisoning off the Japanese coast, which quite properly gave rise to an improvement of methods of testing for mercury all over the world; it is now possible to detect the slight trace of mercury which is normal in seawater, so any water with more mercury than this must be affected by pollution.

The nuclear energy industry makes use of spectrochemical analysis at each and every stage of its processes, from the refining of uranium ore to the testing of the particularly strong steels used in reactors. The products of nuclear fission and other by-products of nuclear energy production are tested in this way, using spectrographic equipment enclosed in specially ventilated areas to avoid any possible risk to the operator who carries out the analysis.

Spectrophotometry For many purposes, it is not necessary to vaporize the sample to observe its emission lines. Instead, the molecular absorption bands are studied by means of a *spectrophotometer*. This provides a graph of absorption against wavelength, the sample usually being liquid or gaseous. The majority of molecular absorption bands of interest are located in the infra-red part of the spectrum, but visible and ultra-violet spectrophotometers are also widely used.

Since the bands being examined are not as sharp as the spectral lines of an emission spectrum, it is possible to use comparatively poor resolution (here, the ability to distinguish between features of nearly the same wavelength), resulting in speedier analysis.

Astronomical spectroscopy Many advances in spectrum theory were made by studying the spectra of stars and nebulae, where matter exists in states impossible to produce in the laboratory. It is true to say that spectroscopy has had as much effect on ASTROPHYSICS and our knowledge of the universe as the telescope itself. Spectra are altered by various conditions at their source, such as pressure, temperature, turbulence, magnetic and electric fields and motion (detected by the DOPPLER EFFECT), as well as by the chemical compositions of the bodies themselves. It is possible, by looking at more and more distant objects, to determine how the chemical composition of the universe has changed over its lifetime, since the light left the most distant objects long before the Earth itself was formed.

SPECTROSCOPY, MASS (see mass spectroscopy)

SPECTRUM (see electromagnetic radiation and prism)

SPEED (see dynamics)

SPEEDOMETER

The speedometer is the device on the dashboard of the car which indicates two things: the speed of the vehicle and total distance travelled. It may also have a 'trip' facility whereby the distance travelled on a journey may be shown.

The type of speedometer fitted to cars, motorcycles, and the majority of commercial vehicles since World War 2 is the magnetic speedometer, originally developed in the 1920s.

Speed indication The speedometer is driven from a point on the vehicle transmission which is rotating at a speed directly proportional to road speed; there is often a specially provided point on the gearbox tail shaft. Drive transmission is by means of a flexible shaft of multi-strand wire rotating inside a flexible tube. This assembly is called the *flexible drive*, or more commonly, the *speedometer cable*.

The flexible drive is connected to the main spindle of the speedometer, which carries a magnet. Close to this magnet, and pivoted on the same axis, is an aluminium disc or cup called the *drag cup*. This is connected directly to the indicator or pointer. On the other side of the drag cup from the magnet is a steel stator; when the vehicle moves, the magnet rotates, creating a magnetic FIELD, and the stator is rotated. Although the aluminium drag cup is non-magnetic, it is conductive; the magnetic field causes an EDDY CURRENT in the cup thus creating a force field. This causes the cup to try to follow the rotation of the magnet, but it is restrained by a hairspring. As speed increases, the *torque* (see DYNAMICS and STATICS) on the drag cup also increases and overcomes the hairspring reaction,

SMITHS INDUSTRIES LTD

causing the pointer to move around the scale on the dial.

Type of indication
The most common type of speedometer uses a pointer on a circular or arc scale, but sometimes the design calls for a coloured line moving along a horizontal or vertical straight scale. This effect can be achieved in two ways with the magnetic speedometer. In one instance the drag cup is linked directly to a tube on which is printed a coloured helix. This is positioned behind a slot in the dial so that when it is turned by the drag cup the helix advances along the scale, giving the appearance of a moving strip of colour. An alternative means of providing a similar effect is the *ribbon* speedometer, which is more common in Britain. In this instrument the drag cup is linked by nylon cords to two vertically pivoted drums between which is wound a tape, printed half black and half red. In the static condition the red portion of the tape is wound around the left hand drum and held there by hairspring tension. As speed increases the drag cup winds the tape on to the right hand drum, so that the leading edge of the red portion appears in the slot on the dial.

Odometer
The odometer is a COUNTING DEVICE which acts as a DISTANCE RECORDER. It comprises a series of adjacent rotating drums or counters each numbered 0 to 9, positioned behind a slot in a dial so that only one number on each counter is showing at any one time. Hidden between the counters are tiny double-sided plastic transfer pinions, which are mounted eccentrically to the main counter axis on thin carrier plates, which in turn are anchored so that they cannot turn with the counters.

The transfer pinion has two sets of teeth engaging, one on each side, with the internal gearing on the counters. The internal gearing of the counter has twenty teeth on one side and just two 'knockover' teeth on the other. Each time a counter comes up to the '9' position, a knockover tooth engages with the transfer pinion to the right, and drives it far enough to rotate it one tenth of a turn, before disengaging.

Where a 'trip' facility is provided, the transfer pinions are mounted externally to the counters on a spring-loaded spindle, which allows them to disengage when the counters are reset to zero.

Calibration
Drive to the counters can be provided by a system of worm-geared shafts driven from the main spindle of the speedometer, if the manufacturer does not wish to vary the ratio between distance travelled and turns of the speedometer cable. The ratio is usually 1000 turns to a mile. In some cases, however, car makers want to be able to alter the axle ratio or the tyre size without changing the pinion in the gearbox which drives the speedometer. To accommodate this need, the counters are driven through an eccentric spindle geared to the main spindle and carrying a pawl which engages with a ratchet wheel. By varying the number of teeth and the throw of the eccentric, variations in gear ratio can be provided.

Calibration of the speed indication part of the instrument to suit each vehicle manufacturer's requirements on gearing and accuracy is carried out by fully magnetizing the magnet and then demagnetizing it until the desired readings are obtained.

Left: a typical speedometer. The counting device is the odometer, or mileage counter; the numbers show through a slot in the dial.

Below left: this design, called a ribbon speedometer, has a coloured line indicator instead of a pointer. The advancing coloured line is provided by a tape which is stored, like a typewriter ribbon, on the drums at each end of the device. As speed increases, the instrument winds the tape on to the right-hand drum against spring pressure, allowing the red line to show through a slot.

Right: the mechanism. The speedometer cable turns the shaft, which has a short worm on it, operating the odometer by means of a ratchet. The internal teeth in the odometer are arranged so that one revolution of a counter turns the next counter one-tenth of a revolution. A permanent magnet on the shaft turns the drag cup, stator, and hence the pointer, against the pressure of the spring.

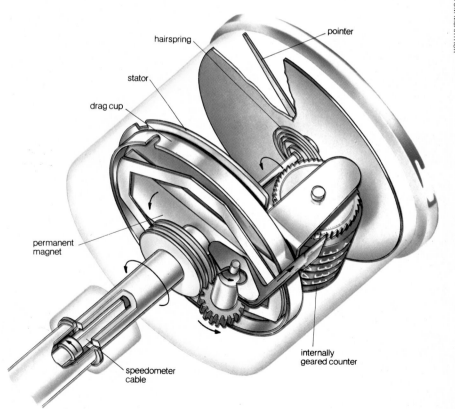

TOM McARTHUR

hairspring

pointer

stator

drag cup

permanent magnet

speedometer cable

internally geared counter

SPERRY, Elmer Ambrose (1860–1930)

Elmer Ambrose Sperry was born in Cortland, New York on 12 October 1860, and is perhaps best known as one of the early pioneers in the study and application of the GYROSCOPE to navigation, stabilization and control of ships and aircraft. This was not, however, his only interest and more than 400 patents on a great variety of subjects were issued in his name.

Sperry attended the State Normal School at Cortland and later was a special student at Cornell University studying generators (see ALTERNATOR and DYNAMO) and ARC LAMPS.

In 1887 he married Zula Goodman, daughter of the Deacon of the Baptist Church in Chicago, and subsequently had four children. Elmer Sperry's aptitude for electrical devices was soon apparent and his early inventions in the period 1883 to 1890 include generators, arc lights, mining machinery, electric locomotives, trams [streetcars] and an electric automobile. All his inventions included innovations which were the subject of numerous patent applications.

Several companies were started bearing Sperry's name to exploit the different devices, and one by one the majority of the patents and companies were assigned or passed to other companies.

In the early 1900s Sperry's interest was taken by the gyroscope and the possibilities of using it to stabilize automobiles and then ships (see STABILIZER) and also its use as a GYRO-COMPASS.

In 1911 he was awarded a naval contract to fit his stabilizer to the USS *Warden*. The installation consisted of two electrically driven 50 inch (1.27 m) diameter wheels, each weighing 4000 pounds (1.8 tons). Other installations for naval and merchant ships followed, culminating in a massive three gyro

SPERRY

Above : Elmer Sperry, whose invention of the gyrocompass in the 1900s led to the development of the inertial guidance and navigation systems now used by aircraft, ships, missiles and spacecraft.

wheel installation in the Italian liner *Conte di Savoia*. Each wheel weighed 110 tons and was 13 ft (4 m) in diameter. Although it effectively stabilized the ship, the problems of expense and weight associated with this type of stabilizer were such that no further installations were made.

During this same period, Sperry turned his attention to the gyrocompass. By 1911 his gyrocompass was undergoing sea trials on the USS *Delaware*. The United States Government placed orders for six compasses and within a month this was increased by a further ten to sixteen compasses.

By 1913 Sperry had set up an office in London and the Sperry gyrocompass was being tested by the Admiralty on a battleship, the HMS *St Vincent* and HM Submarine E1. The successful results of the test led to the Royal Navy adopting the new compass. Orders were also received from the Russian, Italian and French Navies.

To meet an enormous demand for the gyrocompass created by the onset of World War 1, not only was production speeded up in America but the Sperry Gyroscope Company Ltd was incorporated by 1914 in London to manufacture gyrocompasses for the British and other world navies. After the war, the compass was taken up by the world's merchant marine, and it was followed in 1922 by 'Metal Mike', a device that enabled ships to hold course automatically; the forerunner of today's gyro-pilots. Also at this time, Sperry returned to his earlier work and developed a high intensity searchlight five times brighter than the previous best searchlight available. The new searchlight was widely used during World War 1 and after.

During this time, the new technology of powered flight was progressing, and again Elmer Sperry applied himself to its problems. In 1909 he had started work on an aeroplane stabilizer based on similar principles to his ship's stabilizers, but this was later abandoned in favour of a more advanced system where four gyroscopes provided the basic references for stable flight and the control surfaces of the aircraft were operated by compressed air servo motors (see SERVO-MECHANISM).

The stabilizer was first fitted to a Curtiss seaplane in 1912. Both Sperry and his son Lawrence, who had by then joined him in business, became deeply involved in the development of the stabilizer, which was to tax their skill to the utmost. Development continued with assistance from the US Navy.

Success finally crowned Elmer and Lawrence's efforts when in 1914 a spectacular demonstration flight in a French War Department Competition on air safety proved the effectiveness of the Sperry Aeroplane Stabilizers. During and after the war Elmer Sperry turned his attention to attitude and azimuth flight INSTRUMENTS, but it was not until the late 1920s that a successful directional gyro and an artificial horizon were achieved. During this period, Elmer Sperry spent a great deal of time on developing a compound DIESEL ENGINE for use in aircraft and for a DIESEL-ELECTRIC engine for locomotives. After several years, however, the project was finally abandoned, owing mainly to the lack of materials that would withstand the high pressures and temperatures generated in his engine.

The last years of his life were mainly taken up with the development of rail track recorder gyros to check the level and alignment of rails, and a rail flaw detector. Both designs were highly successful and widely used in America.

Zula, Sperry's wife, died in March 1930 after contracting pneumonia during a voyage on the SS *Mauretania*. Three months later, after a gallstone operation, Sperry died in a Brooklyn hospital on 16 June 1930.

SPINNING

The basic principles of spinning involve taking a mass of un-spun fibres, thinning them out (*drawing out*), twisting them into a thread and *winding* them on to bobbins. All natural fibres other than silk—wool, flax (termed linen when converted to yarn), cotton and the coarser fibres such as jute and hemp are spun on these principles, but the machinery details are very different for each group. All require preparatory processes before they are suitable for the actual spinning operation, such as loosening, disentangling, removing impurities, straightening and to some degree arranging the fibres in parallel order.

During these processes the drawing out operation generally continues throughout the sequences, and in the later stages (although there are exceptions) is accomplished by the use of drawing or *drafting* rollers. These consist of pairs of rollers arranged in a row, between which the material, now in the form of a flat ribbon, is conveyed. Each succeeding pair of rollers turns more quickly, pulling the fibres slightly apart, and the ribbon becomes thinner still, so that it needs a little twist to keep the fibres together. It is now called *slubbing* or *roving*.

Before this stage is reached, however, in some sections of the industry a process termed *combing* is carried out. It is literally a combing action in which rows of metal teeth penetrate the material, move through it, and leave the fibres in a much straighter and more nearly parallel order than do any of the other processes. This is generally required when finer and smoother yarns are needed.

The process of spinning was carried on for many hundreds of years by manual methods. Towards the end of the 18th century, various types of machines were invented to carry out the operations that were previously done by hand. The basic procedures are still the same, and the machines have the same names, though their size and quality has improved.

Flyer spinning frame   This was invented by Richard Arkwright in 1769 and was the first to embody drawing rollers. Because for many years the machines were driven by water wheels, they became known as *water frames*. Although others claimed to have been the originators of these rollers, the fact remains that only Arkwright made them a practical success, and there is little doubt that this resulted only after years of trial and experiment. Important factors such as the spacings between adjacent pairs of rollers in relation to the fibre lengths of the cotton he used, the nature of the roller surfaces and the pressures between the top and bottom rollers had to be considered. These pressures were obtained by weighting the top rollers, using hooks which hung from them and supported the weights hanging below. The modern versions of the machine are much larger and in many ways different, but the principles of the processing are the same as in Arkwright's day.

The twisting and winding operations in the machine are continuous. The roving leaves the drawing rollers and passes down one leg of a *flyer*, through an eyelet and on to the bobbin. The flyer is in the form of an inverted U, attached to and rotating with a spindle, which is turned by a short driving belt. The bobbin is also on the spindle but free to rotate separately. Actually it is turned by the pull of the yarn being wrapped round it by the flyer, and as the yarn is being continuously delivered by the rollers. Because of the high speeds, the bobbins gather momentum and tend to over-run. To prevent this brakes are applied in the form of rough surfaced discs on which the bobbins rest. Flyer spinning frames are used extensively in the wool, flax and jute industries.

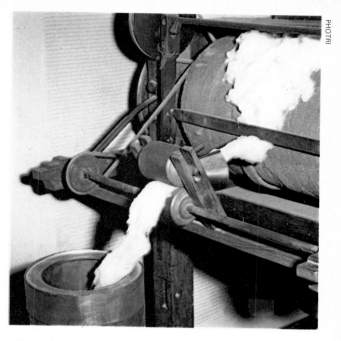

Above: this carding machine of 1790 shows clearly the sort of process required to produce cotton in a form suitable for machines.

Below: a cap spinner, used for the production of worsted (woollen) yarns for weaving into suiting. Most of these machines have now been replaced by ring frames, though a few are still in use.

Spinning mule This machine is classed as an intermittent spinner: that is, the drawing out and twisting are carried out as a separate operation to that of winding, since the first two processes cease while the winding takes place. The machine was invented about 1774–9 by Samuel Crompton at his home, the *Hall i' th' Wood*, near Bolton, although he did not apply for a patent. At first the machine was called the *muslin wheel* because of the very fine cotton yarn it produced—yarns which previously had been imported from India, where the natives had been spinning them for centuries. Because it was soon realized that the machine was a combination of or cross between Arkwright's water frame, with its drawing rollers, and HARGREAVES' *jenny*, where the space between the delivery points and the spindles was gradually increased, it soon became known as the *mule*.

The machine consists of the drawing rollers already mentioned, and a row of plain spindles mounted on a large structure on wheels known as the *carriage*. This moves to and fro, towards and away from the drawing rollers over a distance of about six feet (2 m). During the drawing and twisting operations the carriage is at first in a position close to the rollers, while the yarn passes down from the rollers to the spindles, which are situated below the rollers and are inclined to the vertical. This results in the yarn forming a spiral along the spindle and as this rotates at a high speed, the top coil slips off, causing twist to be inserted in the yarn. At the same time, the carriage begins to move away from the rollers at a speed usually slightly higher than the rate of delivery by the rollers, and this process continues until the carriage reaches the end of its outward run. This combination of drawing out and twisting produces a much more even yarn than other machines, since the twist tends to flow to the thinner places, preventing further thinning, while the relatively untwisted thick places are drawn out more. It is an important feature of the mule's action and explains why in addition to the general reduction of friction and excessive strains on the yarn (compared with other spinning machines), the mule produces such fine even and soft yarns.

Before the spun length of yarn can be wound on the spindle (no bobbins being needed) the coils of yarn on the spindles must be removed and this is done by reversing their rotation a few revolutions. At the same time the slack yarn so removed

Above: two views of over 1000 ends of yarn being spun simultaneously on a mule. One machine draws out its yarn while the opposite one winds its spun yarn on to the bobbins. This machine was in use till quite recently, but in almost all types of spinning ring frames are now standard because they can spin larger 'packages' at a time.

Right: spinning is preceded by processes to clean and straighten the fibres. The cotton lint surrounds seeds which are removed in a cotton gin, but the cotton is cleaned further by beating. From this stage the lint is transferred to a thin sheet or lap. It is taken from this by a roller and passed to the carding stage, which makes the fibres more parallel, and is then thinned down by means of drafting rollers, to be deposited in a can as a coil of sliver. The drafting process may take place several times, to thin the sliver down, which can then be spun in any of the three ways shown.

is taken up by a *faller wire* which descends from above the spindles and another which rises from below the yarn; between them they keep the yarns taut.

The carriage now begins to move in towards the rollers, the spindles turn in their original direction and the first faller wire guides the yarn on to the package, which is known as a *cop*, while the second wire maintains the yarn at a suitable tension. When the carriage reaches the rollers, the wires return to their stationary positions and the cycle begins again. Many improvements have been made to the machine since Crompton's day, but it was not till 1830 that it became entirely automatic in action.

Ring spinning frame This is a continuous spinning machine, the invention of which round about the second and third decades of the 19th century has been claimed by several Americans.

Instead of a flyer, the bobbin, fixed to and rotating with the spindle, is surrounded by a non-rotating ring. On the ring is a flange on which has been clipped a small, C-shaped wire termed a *traveller*, which moves quite freely round the ring. The yarn leaving the drawing rollers passes through this traveller and on to the bobbin, and as the latter rotates at high speed so twist is inserted. Winding results because as the yarn pulls the traveller round, so continuous delivery from the rollers causes it to lose speed. Each time it makes one revolution less than the bobbin, a coil is wound on the latter.

OSBORNE/MARKS

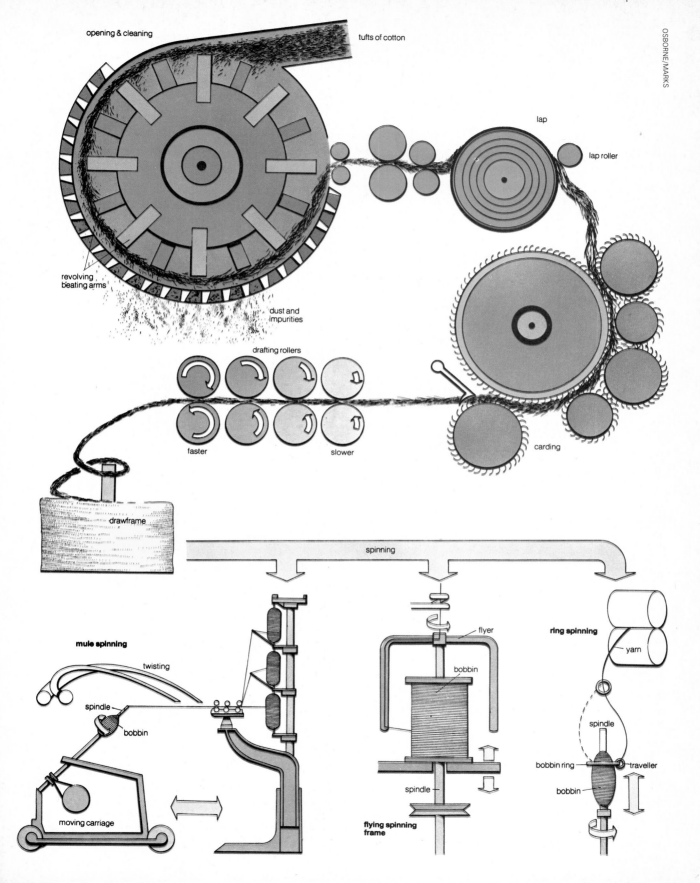

opening & cleaning

tufts of cotton

lap

lap roller

revolving beating arms

dust and impurities

drafting rollers

faster

slower

carding

drawframe

spinning

mule spinning

twisting

spindle

bobbin

moving carriage

flyer

bobbin

spindle

flying spinning frame

ring spinning

yarn

spindle

bobbin ring

traveller

bobbin

The ring frame is used extensively in the cotton industry, and has largely taken the place of the mule except for the production of the finest yarns. This change has taken place mainly because of the costly, highly skilled labour needed to operate the mule, whereas semi-skilled labour is needed to tend the ring frame.

Cap spinning frame   This machine is another American invention dating from about the same period as the invention of the ring frame. A stationary *cap* or hood covers the bobbin, and the yarn, on leaving the drawing rollers, passes under the lower edge of the cap then on to the rotating bobbin. The friction between cap and yarn causes the latter to be retarded, so that winding as well as twisting takes place simultaneously.

Other methods   Although spinning has been defined as the drawing out, twisting and winding of fibres, there are exceptions. One such exception is silk 'spinning', a process carried out by the silk worm, which extrudes a viscous solution from its body in the form of a fine stream which solidifies on contact with the air and becomes a continuous and extremely fine, glossy filament. This the worm winds around itself to form a cocoon, from which it would eventually emerge as a moth if nature were allowed to take its course. As such action would break the continuity of the filaments, however, the chrysalids are killed and cocoons maintained intact. The filaments, often over 100 metres long, are unwound from the cocoons by a process known as *reeling*, the cocoons being softened in heated water to facilitate the unwinding. Later a number of these filaments are wound and twisted together in a process known as *throwing*.

The cocoons cannot be completely unwound, and the remnants are broken up, producing masses of short filaments which are spun on similar principles to those applied in the spinning of cotton. The thrown yarns are termed *nett* and the spun yarns *spun* silk.

Artificial silk yarns, now known as rayon, are also produced by extrusion, as are other man made yarns, such as nylon and Terylene [Dacron] (see FIBRE, SYNTHETIC). Viscous solutions differing chemically for each kind of yarn are forced by pressure through very fine orifices termed *spinnerets*, the process being an imitation of the action of the silk worm. They are solidified by being passed through suitable liquids. Certainly 'extruding' is a more appropriate term for this process, than is 'spinning'. Sometimes, however, the filaments are cut into short lengths and spun by the orthodox methods.

JAPAN SILK ASSOCIATION/TOKYO

COURTAULDS LTD

Above: the source of the raw material used by this reeling machine is visible at the bottom of the picture—the cocoons of silk worms.

Right: a modern ring frame spinning directly from the 'sliver', which in this case consists of manmade fibres. The drawing out rollers are clearly seen. Versions of the ring frame, with its large 'packages', are in widespread use.

SPIRITS

Fermentation is a process whereby sugar is transformed into alcohol by the action of a YEAST. One of the most familiar fermented liquids is WINE, which is made by allowing the natural yeast in the grape skins to act on the natural sugar in the juice. BEER is produced by introducing yeast into a sweetened liquid obtained from a cereal, usually barley. *Spirits* are made by *distilling* fermented liquids: because alcohol is more volatile than water, it distils over more readily and spirits therefore contain more alcohol than the original fermented liquid.

It is not known with certainty who invented DISTILLATION. Claims are made for its introduction to the Indian subcontinent 2000 years ago, possibly from China. It has only been practised in Europe for about half that time, at first for making medicinal preparations and then in the production of perfumes from flower essences. Commercial distillation is not much more than 400 years old. There are two common types of ALCOHOL: *ethanol*, which occurs in alcoholic drinks, and *methanol* (also called industrial or wood alcohol) which is poisonous and comes from a variety of sources.

Distillation is mainly carried out by two forms of still. The best known is the *pot still* or *alembic*, which is like a large kettle, nearly always of copper, tinned on the inside. To this is attached a *condenser*, which cools the spirit-containing vapour and restores it to liquid form. There are various styles of pot still and a great range of sizes; the particular design will depend both on the spirit being distilled—brandy, whisky or gin for example—and on local traditions and regulations. The other type of still is the *patent* or *Coffey still* and the process of distilling with this sort of still is known, accurately, as *continuous distillation*. The patent still employs steam to separate the spirit from the alcoholic wash with which it is charged. The system was invented in Scotland by Robert Stein in 1826 and perfected six years later by Aeneas Coffey. Continuous distillation is used for producing spirits in very large quantities, and the spirit from a patent still is usually very strong, almost flavourless, and highly refined. The spirit from a pot

Below : the production of malt whisky. Barley is first steeped in water and dried in peat smoke to produce malt which is dressed and ground and passed to the malt grist hopper. Water is added to the malt to produce a mash from which wort (a liquid) is separated. Fermentation of the wort and double distillation yields whisky.

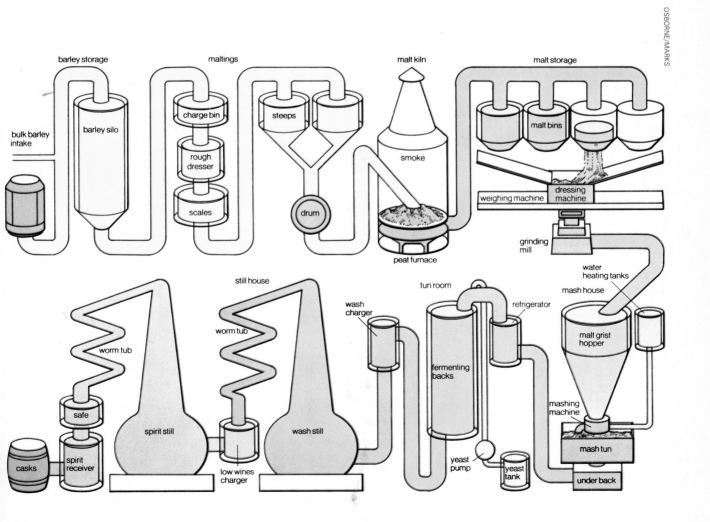

OSBORNE/MARKS

DISTILLERS CO LTD

SUSAN GRIGGS AGENCY/PHOTO: ADAM WOOLFITT

ROBERT HARDING ASSOCIATES

Left: the spirit safe at a whisky distillery in Scotland. Spirit from the stills passes through this safe for sampling before it is re-distilled or put into casks.

Below left: solid waste is removed from a still after distillation of Chartreuse. The liqueur is made near Grenoble, France, by the monks of La Grande Chartreuse. The recipe, said to involve more than 100 different herbs, is a closely guarded secret and has been in the possession of the monks since it was perfected in 1757.

Right: the mash tun at a Scotch whisky distillery. The mash is the basic liquid from which whisky is made: it is fermented and then distilled twice.

Far right: copper stills at a vodka distillery.

still is less strong and carries with it flavour characteristics from the alcoholic wash from which it has been distilled. This is vital for the production of fine spirits with natural and distinctive taste such as good whisky or brandy. But spirit from the pot still also retains some unwanted ingredients called *congeners*: these disappear when it is matured in wooden casks.

Whisky Whisky of a sort is produced all over the world, but the most well known whisky is Scotch whisky. Almost certainly the art of distilling was brought to Scotland from northern Ireland by missionary monks, and the first such distillates would have had medical uses. Whisky is first recorded in Scottish history in 1494. By 1500 it was drunk at the court in Edinburgh and in 1505 the king gave it official recognition by placing its control in the capital in the hands of the Royal College of Surgeons. The word 'whisky' is derived from the Gaelic *uisque beatha* which means 'water of life'. The dropping of the 'e' for Scotch and Canadian whisky, and its retention for other types, is a comparatively modern convention.

After a turbulent history, with the introduction of the patent still, Scotch whisky settled down to legal existence and growth, and around 1860 came the innovation of *blending*. This meant that the pungent pot-distilled *malt whiskies*, largely associated with the Highlands, were mixed with the much lighter *grain whiskies* produced by patent distillation. This new type was infinitely more to the taste of the English, and within a fairly short time Scotch whisky had conquered not just the British market but that of the whole civilized world.

Malt whisky is made wholly from malted barley. *Malting* is the process of steeping barley in water: in the case of Scotch whisky this is the very special water in which the country is rich. When the barley has started to sprout, it is dried and peat smoke is allowed to permeate the drying barley. This is then dressed and ground, more of the famous water is added, and from the resulting *mash* a sweetish liquid (*wort*) is drawn off and cooled. The wort is run into huge vats where it begins

to ferment after yeast has been added, making a sort of beer (*wash*). From this alcoholic wash (about 10% alcohol), which carries the essential characteristics of Scottish water and peat, malt whisky is distilled. There are two distillations; the first produces a weakish and rather rough spirit called *low wines*. This is charged into a second pot still and the result is Scotch malt whisky. Before it becomes lawfully Scotch whisky, however, it must be matured in wood for a minimum period of three years. It is commonly matured for a much longer period.

Grain whisky is produced by continuous distillation from maize to which some malted barley has been added. It is rarely matured for more than three years. Blended Scotch whisky, by far the most popular type, is a mixture of malt and grain whiskies. A good blend will contain about 30 individual malts, whose character will depend very much on the distillery of origin, although at least one famous brand contains over 60 different malts. There is no regulation as to the quantities of grain in a blend, but a fine brand will contain about equal proportions of malts and grain. Some whiskies are re-casked after blending for further maturing in the wood which ensures that the whiskies in the blend are thoroughly married. Eventually the blended whisky will be diluted with purified water to the strength demanded by the market for which it is intended. If a Scotch whisky carries an age, it is the length of time spent in the cask in the case of a straight malt whisky, or, in the case of a blend, the age of the youngest constituent whisky.

There are a great number of legally defined American whiskies, but in international commerce the only important one is *bourbon*, protected from 1964 by Act of Congress. Many aspects of its production are controlled by law, for example it must be produced from a mash containing at least 51% maize and it must be matured in new casks, which ensures that the resulting spirit will have the characteristic strong flavour of bourbon. Its home is Kentucky, but it is produced in several other states of the USA.

Canadian whisky is a lighter spirit than bourbon, but lacks the character of Scotch. Maize is the principal grain in the mash, but some wheat and malted barley are employed. Canadian whisky is very popular in parts of the USA.

Irish whiskey is unique in having a proportion of oats in the mash; also wheat, rye, and barley, of which half is malted. It is mainly a pot still product, and is distilled three times and matured for a minimum of seven years.

Brandy Brandy is defined as a distillate from wine or wine by-products. It is made in all wine producing countries, and some such distillates—which would qualify as brandy in Britain if matured three years—are of extremely poor quality. It is important to differentiate between what the trade call simply *grape brandy* and such distillates as *Cognac*. Grape brandy, whether French or from any other country, may be distilled from any sort of wine, probably by continuous distillation, and sometimes have a little good pot stilled brandy added to give it some character. There is, unfortunately, very little legal significance in words and initials that appear on brandy labels: thus it is in order to put the magic, but meaningless name Napoleon on a simple grape brandy.

The leading brandy of repute is Cognac, a closely controlled product coming only from special areas in south-western France and centering on the towns of Cognac and Jarnac. It is produced under strict regulations. Double distillation is employed, as for Scotch whisky, though the stills are much smaller. The special wine of the district, from which Cognac is distilled, is not matured and is distinctly acid; strangely, from this indifferent wine comes the finest brandy. Like all distillations, the spirit is white when it leaves the stills. It is matured in Limousin oak casks. By an elaborate 'topping up' process, average age is built up. A proportion of each distillation is matured, unblended, for as much as fifty years, when it will improve no more. It is then placed in big bottles, and a little will be added to a brand's oldest blends, giving extra distinction. No Cognac matured in France carries a date. *Vintage Cognac* is a brandy sent to Britain, a year after the vintage from which it was distilled, and matured in England: it is not much seen. A bottle of vintage Cognac should carry the date of the vintage and the date of bottling, for it is the time it spends in cask that counts: no spirit improves in the bottle. The colour of a spirit has nothing to do with its taste or quality: a century or more ago the French brandy sold in Britain was quite dark, but then a fashion for a lighter Cognac came in—hence VSOP (Very Special Old Pale). Although spirits will pick up varying amounts of colour from cask maturing—quite a lot in the case of old malt whisky but much less for Cognac—commercially, colour adjustment is required to retain a brand's standard. This does not affect flavour in any way.

The other great quality French brandy is *Armagnac*, produced slightly further south. Production is about a quarter that of Cognac and it is much less well-known. Armagnac is a single distillation and thus highly flavoured. It requires long maturing to achieve perfection, but can then be very fine indeed.

Rum To be so named, rum must be distilled from the by-product of the production of cane sugar in a cane sugar producing country. The British market is almost wholly supplied from the British West Indies. Though a few special rums are distilled in pot stills, nearly all rums in commerce are from patent stills. When water is added to molasses (residue of cane sugar production), natural yeasts start a speedy fermentation, and from the resultant alcoholic wash an extremely clean spirit, often called *cane spirit*, is distilled. To make dark rum, other than extra quality grades, concentrate of rum flavouring and flavourless colouring matter are added to the white distillate. People expect traditional heavy (Navy style) rums to be dark, but they are not pungent because they are dark; it is simply a tradition.

Vodka Vodka is the national drink of Russia and Poland. Literally translated the word means 'little water'. It can be made from a variety of sources including potatoes, wheat, rye, sugar beet or a mixture of these. After distillation the spirit is thoroughly purified by filtration through charcoal, diluted with water and then bottled without undergoing any ageing. Vodka made in this way is only very slightly flavoured and is designed to be drunk ice cold, but in the homelands of vodka, numerous flavours are infused into the drink; for example, in Poland *żubrówka* is made by flavouring vodka with a type of grass.

Gin Britain's second most popular spirit began life in Holland, where it first appeared as a medicinal preparation around 1550. Dutch gin is now markedly different from the best known type, *London Dry* gin (nowadays the name denotes a type of gin rather than its place of origin). In 19th century England gin was produced in large quantities and was sold very cheaply; it became the despised intoxicant of the urban masses. Now, however, it is a universally esteemed spirit and the prime constituent of many of the world's favourite mixed drinks. The international reputation of London's gin started with the introduction there about a century ago of 'unsweetened gin' which marked the separation of what was to become known as London Dry from its heavier Netherlands precursor.

In Britain and the USA, gin is produced from a purified grain spirit by re-distilling it in a pot still in the presence of various botanical extracts, the most important being essence of juniper, from which gin derives its name. Other botanical flavourings include coriander, liquorice, orris, cardamon, anise, fennel, bitter almonds, lemon peel and so on: precisely which ingredients are used and in what proportion will depend on the particular brand. Related to gin is *schnapps* from Holland and the Scandinavian drink *aquavit*.

Liqueurs A liqueur is a spirit which has been sweetened and flavoured with herbs, fruits or a mixture of both. It would take a book to list all the liqueurs of the world, for in some countries almost every village has its own distinctive liqueur. Most liqueurs are made by flavouring a spirit base, for example Cognac, with an infusion of the flavouring material, although sometimes the flavouring is added before distillation. While the recipe of most liqueurs is a closely guarded secret, many have a single predominant flavour, for example green Chartreuse (liquorice), yellow Chartreuse (anise), Cointreau (orange), Crème de Menthe (mint), Curaçao (orange), Grand Marnier (orange), Irish Mist (honey), Kahlúa (cocoa-coffee), Kümmel (caraway), Maraschino (cherry), Ojen (anise), Ouzo (anise), Sabra (chocolate), Tia Maria (coffee) and Triple Sec (orange). Other liqueurs have distinctive spicy flavours which cannot easily be associated with a particular source; these include Bénédictine, Drambuie, Galliano and Strega.

All drinks mentioned above are spirits of one sort or another, but the list is by no means complete. Virtually wherever there is some vegetable matter that will ferment there will be a distilled spirit derived from it. Other well known spirits include the cactus based *tequila* of Mexico, *slivovitz*, the plum brandy of central Europe, *kirsch* from cherries, *calvados* distilled from cider, and *pisco*, the basic distilled spirit of South America.

Below : a view of the pot stills in a modern gin distillery. Gin is made by re-distilling a purified spirit to which various flavourings, particularly juniper, have been added.

DISTILLERS CO LTD

SPORTS EQUIPMENT

The origins of some games are lost in the past (golf, for instance, appears to have originated in the 15th century), but others were developed over a short period in more recent times. Because of basic differences in the nature of games, equipment used varies considerably in shape, size and constitution and manufacturing methods differ accordingly. The adoption of new materials and manufacturing techniques is severely limited by the rules governing the games which are often designed to preserve traditional aspects. For instance, the resilience of golf balls made in the USA (and hence flight distance) is strictly limited, and such a rule is likely to be introduced worldwide.

Wood and leather, being natural materials, have been used for many years for golf, tennis, cricket equipment and so on, and there is still a considerable requirement for these materials. Newer materials such as high strength ALLOYS, RUBBER, PLASTICS, GLASS and CARBON FIBRE are now also used in large quantities.

Tennis balls
Tennis (or lawn tennis to give its correct name) was developed from *real* or *royal* tennis, a game going back to the 14th century. Lawn tennis was perfected in the 1870s and was based on a ball made of rubber which bounced considerably better than the cloth-stuffed ball used for real tennis. Covering the rubber with felt was found to improve its wearing qualities. The felt seams were originally joined by stitching, but this was replaced by rubber cement in the 1920s.

The modern manufacturing method consists of first mixing rubber with special ingredients (clay to reinforce, sulphur and 'accelerators' for vulcanization) in an 'internal' mixer which consists of a pair of intermeshing rotors rotating within a chamber, which continuously shear the rubber-powder mixture until it is homogeneously blended. The mixture or *compound*, which is of putty-like consistency, is then forced by hydraulic pressure through the circular die of an extruder to produce a continuous rod, which is chopped into pieces or *plugs* of identical size and weight by a high speed rotating knife. Each plug is then placed into a cavity of a multi-cavity forming mould which squeezes it under hydraulic pressure into a hollow hemispherical shape which makes one half of a tennis ball. Heat is also applied so that the rubber becomes *vulcanized*— that is, converted from a putty-like material to an elastic material. Each hemispherical shell is stamped out from the excess 'flash' and two hemispheres are joined together with rubber cement to form a *core* (rubber ball). The core may be pressurized with air or gas to 10 to 12 psi (0.7 to 0.8 bar) above atmospheric pressure, or alternatively may be of the 'pressureless' variety. (In the latter case the bouncing qualities are obtained solely from the rubber of the core, which must be thicker and specially compounded for the purpose.) Most balls are pressurized because they are generally preferred by good tennis players; the usual method of pressurization is to

Below, left: an old French photograph illustrating a type of craftsmanship which is now forgotten: beginning to rough out billiard balls from blocks of ivory. They are now made of plastic.

Below: circular pieces of a putty-like compound are vulcanized into half-round shapes, two of which, when cemented together, make a tennis ball.

include a chemical inflation pellet of sodium nitrite and ammonium chloride when the two hemispheres are glued together. When heat is applied, the pellet decomposes, releasing nitrogen gas.

The felt or *melton* with which a tennis ball is covered is a high quality cloth of wool and nylon. The *weft* (transverse) yarns are made from a wool and nylon mixture and these are woven into the *warp* (longitudinal) yarns, which are cotton, in such a way that the weft appears predominantly on one side of the cloth. This surface is subject to a teaseling or 'raising' operation to produce a hairy surface which is then consolidated by *fulling*—a process in which the natural felting properties of the wool are exploited by working the cloth in a soap solution to produce the necessary surface texture.

The melton is coated with rubber solution on its reverse side and is then cut into dumb-bell shapes, two of which are used together to completely cover the surface of the core. The dumb-bell 'covers' are applied by hand and the degree of stretching is carefully controlled so that an exact fit is obtained. Rubber cement applied to the edges of the dumb-bells becomes vulcanized in a further moulding operation in which the ball is heated in spherical moulds. A steaming operation raises the nap and the ball is tested for deformation under load, so that balls are matched together before they are packaged.

Tennis balls must fulfil a rigid specification determining size, weight, rebound and compression, and careful quality control must be carried out at all stages of the manufacturing operation.

Golf balls Golf balls were originally made by stuffing feathers into a hand stitched leather case under considerable pressure. From 1850, they were made from solid *gutta percha* (a substance related to rubber, coming from the juices of Malayan trees) until the rubber-cored ball was developed about 1900, and this rapidly became accepted after it was used by the winner of the Open Championship in 1902.

The rules of golf lay down only the maximum weight (1.62 oz) and minimum size for a golf ball: 1.62 inch (4.11 cm) in England and elsewhere except the North American Continent, where it is 1.68 inch (4.27 cm) and a maximum resilience is also specified.

A golf ball consists of 3 main components which are a *centre* (usually liquid or resilient rubber) around which are placed *windings* of highly elastic rubber thread and a *cover* to protect the thread and to incorporate the 'dimple' pattern.

A considerable amount of the mass of the ball is concentrated in its centre, which must allow the windings to distort readily when the ball is struck by the club, so that the subsequent rapid recovery of the highly tensioned thread creates high ball velocity. Because the centre must, however, absorb a minimum amount of energy at ball-club contact, the liquid centre has been used in premium balls for many years.

One way of making a liquid centre is as follows. Fine clay is mixed into water and glycerine and the mixture is measured out into hemispherical cavities in rubber moulds. Because of the *thixotropic* (a tendency to become thinner when stirred or shaken but having a high viscosity when undisturbed—a

Above left: the tennis ball covering is made of a high-quality cloth treated to produce a hairy surface. Two dumb-bell shaped pieces are stretched and fitted by hand, using rubber cement.

Left: a final moulding operation finishes the tennis ball. The balls are usually pressurized by means of a chemical pellet which decomposes into a gas when heated inside the ball.

property of certain fluids and plastic solids) nature of the mix-ture, the rubber moulds can be brought together in a vertical orientation so that spheres of paste are produced. The moulds are refrigerated to freeze the spheres of paste and these are then removed and coated with rubber and subjected to a hot moulding operation to vulcanize the rubber coating. The result is a small, heavy, deformable sphere of liquid inside a rubber envelope.

Rubber thread is produced by mixing rubber with special ingredients to obtain a highly elastic sheet after vulcanization —this process being carried out by winding the sheet on to large drums which are put into steam-heated chambers. The sheet is then passed between multi-knife cutters to produce rubber thread of dimensions approximately .060 × .020 inch (1.52 × 0.51 mm).

The golf ball core is made by stretching the rubber thread to about 900% and winding it on to the centre by means of a *core winding* machine. The core is held between high speed rotating rollers which both rotate the core and also allow it to turn about any axis. The operation of the machine causes the stretched thread to be wound on to the smallest diameter

Left: this ingenious machine turns the centre of the golf ball.— a sphere of liquid which is enclosed in a rubber envelope — while the rubber thread, stretched 900%, is wrapped around it.

Below: the golf ball has a small, heavy, deformable centre which must absorb a minimum of energy when struck by the club. The centre is covered with rubber thread windings which are stretched as they are wound on. The compression-moulded cover has dimples which are aerodynamically important for flight distance.

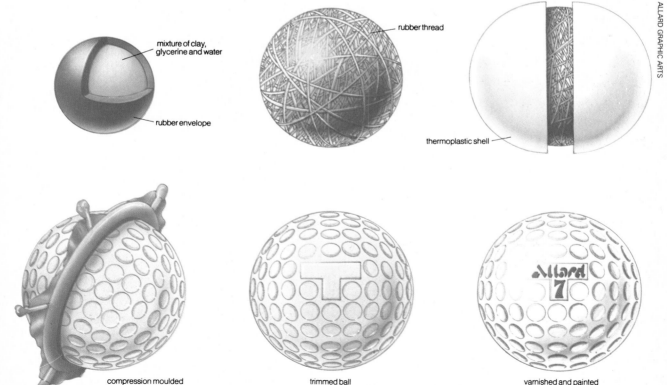

mixture of clay, glycerine and water

rubber envelope

rubber thread

thermoplastic shell

compression moulded

trimmed ball

varnished and painted

DUNLOP SPORTS CO LTD

of the core at any one time, and the core continuously re-orientates itself and so becomes spherical. The machine cuts out automatically when the core grows to the correct size.

The material to form the cover of the ball is a thermoplastic material which is formed into hemispherical *shells* on an injection moulding machine in which the hot, plastic material is forced under pressure into cold moulds. Two shells are placed around each core and the assemblies are inserted into precision dies in a compression moulding press, which moulds the cover material on to the cores under the action of heat and pressure. The dimple pattern is moulded into the surface of the ball by the profiled surface of the die.

The moulds are cooled and the balls extracted and accurately trimmed free of excess material. Pre-paint treatment follows and the balls are spray-painted on machines adapted for painting spherical objects. The balls are matched for compression (that is, deformation under load), the low compression (or high deformation) balls being segregated as lower grade. The balls are identified by a stamping process and finally coated with clear polyurethane lacquer.

The dimple pattern moulded into the ball surface has a very important function and the size and shape of the dimples are critical. The golf club is designed to produce a 'backspin' to the ball at contact—so that although the ball is projected forward, it is also caused to spin about a horizontal axis so that the top of the ball is moving against the direction in which the ball is travelling. The air flow over the top of the ball is therefore speeded up and that below the ball is retarded. This produces a local reduction of air pressure immediately above the ball and an increase in that immediately below the ball such that a resultant upward force or *lift* occurs. The dimple pattern controls the degree of lift generated by influencing the inter-

action between the ball surface and the air flow, and it also affects the 'drag' experienced by the ball in moving through the air. The distance the ball travels through the air is therefore directly dependent on the dimple pattern and a considerable amount of experimentation has been carried out over the years to produce the most efficient pattern in terms of flight distance.

Tennis rackets A tennis racket is not subject to any specification by the rules of lawn tennis but appropriate shapes, sizes, weights and balances have become established by common practice.

Until the 1920s, racket frames were made by bending single sawn sticks of ash to the familiar racket shape after they had been softened by steaming. Subsequently, similar types of frame were produced by steam bending several thinner sticks and gluing them together to produce a *plied* frame. In the 1930s and 40s a process was developed for producing frames from even thinner sticks or veneers which could be bent cold, and strength was improved by adopting urea formaldehyde glues. This is the basis of the laminated wooden frame which we know today.

Various woods are used in each frame. The basic strength of the frame is provided by ash and beech, but the throat or *wedge* area is usually either sycamore or mahogany. Lightweight obeche is used as a spacer in the handle region, and hickory may be used to give strength and wear resistance on the outside of the frame. In some cases, a wood such as walnut is used for its decorative appearance.

The sticks or veneers are obtained from specially selected logs by sawing, slicing or peeling. Peeling is more efficient in yield of wood. In this operation, the log is steamed for a considerable time, and is then rotated about its axis while a con-

Left: strips of wood are bent cold and glued with urea formaldehyde adhesive. The gluing takes place in a forming jig under hydraulic pressure; then the assembly is passed through an oven to set the glue. The 'bends' (strips) are wide enough for three tennis rackets to be cut longitudinally from each bend.

Right: a multi-spindle drilling machine is used to drill all of the stringing holes at once in the perimeter of the racket.

Below: the stringing is done with the help of a machine. In this photo, the application of paint, transfers and lacquer has been done but the rubber grip still needs to be fitted. Wooden tennis rackets outnumber other types by ten to one. Strings for tournament tennis rackets are still made of gut, but nylon is also used. String tension is up to 60 lb (27 kg).

tinuous veneer of wood is pared away by a knife blade which contacts the log along its whole length. The veneer is cut into strips parallel to the grain, which are bent to form the basic 'keyhole' contour of the frame, so that the grain of the wood is used most effectively for strength and rigidity. Shaped pieces for the throat and handle are specially profiled and all the components are coated on mating surfaces with urea formaldehyde glue. They are then assembled into a *bending jig* and the characteristic racket shape is produced by the application of hydraulic pressure, which bends and consolidates the component parts around a *former*. Clamps are attached so that the formed *bend* may be removed from the jig and passed through ovens to cure the adhesive.

In modern manufacturing practice, up to three racket frames can be cut longitudinally from one bend. Handle pieces are then glued on together with reinforcement in the shoulder area and the frame is then subject to a succession of shaping and sanding operations. Stringing holes are produced on a multi-spindle drilling machine, and subsequent countersinking and grooving operations are carried out largely by hand. The application of transfers, painting and lacquering complete the process of manufacture.

Wooden squash and badminton rackets are manufactured in a similar manner, but often such rackets incorporate a steel shaft for improved lightness and strength.

While tennis rackets are also made from steel and aluminium alloys, composite metal and glass fibre and carbon fibre constructions, such rackets are considerably more expensive than wooden ones. Wooden rackets are preferred by the majority of the top-class tournament players and outnumber the other types by about 10 to 1. Metal-headed badminton rackets have substantially replaced wooden ones due to their improved strength and lower weight but in the case of squash rackets, only wooden headed frames are allowed by the rules of the game.

Racket strings are made from natural gut (produced from the intestines of sheep) and although such strings are preferred for top-class tennis, strings made from nylon filaments by a spinning or braiding process are popular because of lower cost and improved durability. Typical stringing tensions are 55 to 60 pounds (25 to 27 kg) for a tennis racket, 35 to 40 pounds (16 to 18 kg) for a squash racket and 25 to 30 pounds (11 to 14 kg) for a badminton racket.

Golf clubs   Golf clubs are subject to certain specifications regarding their general constitution designed to 'preserve the character of the game' and certain aspects such as face markings and grip shapes are closely specified.

The rules allow the golfer to use a set of not more than fourteen clubs; these would typically consist of 4 woods, 9 irons and a putter. Clubs vary in weight (mainly determined by the head), length (determined by the shaft) and *loft*, which is the angle the face of the club makes with the vertical in the address position. Clubs get shorter, heavier and more lofted in their numbered sequence.

The heads of wooden clubs were once largely made from persimmon but nowadays are made from specially shaped laminated blocks of maple, shaped so that the alignment of the laminations changes to maximize the directional strength in the *hosel* area where the shaft is inserted. The heads are turned on a copy LATHE to produce the rough shape characteristic of a golf wood, and areas are routed out on the hitting surface

(*face*) and base (*sole*) to allow the fitting of a plastic facepiece and metal soleplate respectively. The weight of the wooden head is adjusted by adding lead to a hole drilled in the sole before the baseplate is screwed into position. The wood surface is sanded and painted after carefully shaping the club face.

Iron heads were originally hand forged but now are either drop-forged (see FORGING) or cast by an investment CASTING process. In this process the metal is poured into a ceramic mould which is often made from a wax master (lost wax process). Mild steel is primarily used for forged heads, but stainless steels are common in castings. Castings have the advantage that they can be produced to closer tolerances than forgings and allow more design freedom for weight distribution and intricate detail. Additionally, the hole for shaft attachment may be cast rather than drilled. The heads are subject to grinding and polishing operations to produce correct weight and a high surface finish, and are sometimes chromium plated.

In early days shafts were made of split ash and later hickory. Tubular metal shafts date from the 1890s but were not exploited until the early 1920s; although they gained acceptance in USA, they were not authorized for golf in England until 1929. Shafts are now produced from steel alloy (manganese-boron) in tapered form by a step-tapering process in which metal tube is forced through dies of progressively smaller diameter over reducing length of the shaft to produce the characteristic

Below: the manufacture of top-quality sporting goods still requires a great deal of old-fashioned craftsmanship. Cricket balls are still hand-stitched for best quality.

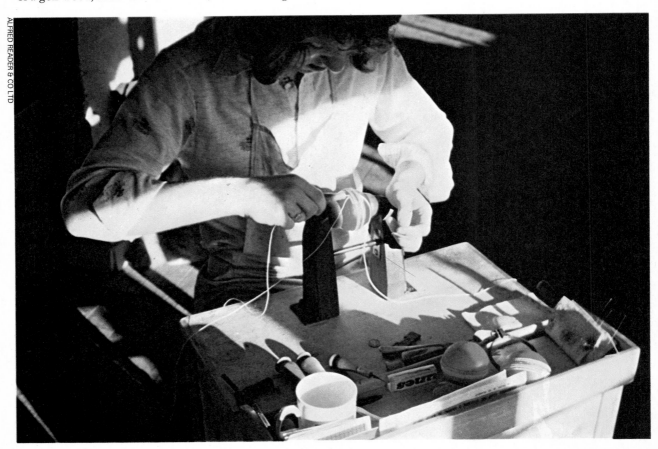

ALFRED READER & CO LTD

'stepped-taper' effect. By this means the appropriate distribution of *flex* is obtained and the smaller diameter of the shaft where it is attached to the head has a thickened wall for improved strength. Different overall stiffness can also be produced by changing the wall thickness of the original tube.

Golf shafts have also been made from other materials, notably aluminium and carbon fibre. The object is to produce shafts of lighter weight than steel shafts and hence produce a more efficient club, but aluminium allowed only a marginal improvement in this respect. Carbon fibre allows a 30% reduction in shaft weight and some of this weight can be transferred to the clubhead with a resultant improvement in ball velocity after impact. Because, however, the fibres must be aligned for satisfactory longitudinal stiffness, torsional properties of carbon fibre shafts tend to be poor and this can adversely affect the golf shot.

The shafts are cut to the appropriate length and glued or riveted to the head. Leather or rubber grips are then fitted and the balance or *swing-weight* of the club, about a point 6 inches (15.2 cm) from the top of the grip, is measured so that sets of matched clubs can be made up.

Other equipment
Although the manufacture of golf and tennis balls, golf clubs and tennis rackets involves modern scientific technology, equipment for other games often requires the skill of craftsmen that has remained unchanged for over

Below : a craftsman using a spokeshave on a cricket bat. The blade is made of willow which is allowed to dry naturally and then compressed for strength; the handle is made from cane and rubber.

a hundred years. The manufacture of leather footballs is one example in which the only concession to modern technology is the use of sewing machines for stitching the casing, although hand stitching is still necessary to complete the work. In the case of cricket balls the best quality ones are still hand-stitched.

Cricket bat making is another area in which the skill of the craftsman is still much in evidence. A *cleft* from which the bat blade is made is roughly split from willow, sawn into lengths and allowed to dry naturally by stacking in open sheds. The face and edges of the blade are then compressed to impart extra toughness. Sarawak cane is planed down and glued together with rubber insertions to form the bat handle which is finished by turning to shape on a lathe. A V-cut is made in the top of the blade and the handle end is shaped to accurately fit and is glued into position. The bat blade is then shaped by means of a drawknife and spokeshave (a two handled planing tool for curved surfaces) to its traditional form, and finally twine and a rubber sleeve is put on the handle. The laws of the game decree that the bat must not be longer than 38 inches (0.965 m) or wider than 4½ inches (11.43 cm) at its widest part.

The method of manufacture of a hockey stick has much in common with that of a cricket bat in that sarawak cane is used for the handle and this is jointed to the head in a similar manner to the *splicing* of a cricket bat handle. The head of a hockey stick is usually of mulberry-wood, which is bent to the familiar shape after steaming. The stick must pass through a 2 inch (5.08 cm) diameter ring to be legal.

SPRAY CAN (see aerosol)

SPRAY GUN

The origin of the spray gun can be attributed to Dr DeVilbiss, a medical practitioner of Toledo, Ohio, USA, who in the early 1800s searched for the ideal method of applying medication to oral and nasal passages. As an alternative to swabbing, the ATOMIZER was devised as a means of introducing a liquid from a container into an air stream which was directed on to the area to be treated, and after a period the atomizer evolved into the PAINT spray gun which is now widely used throughout industry. The spray gun is used to apply coatings such as paints, lacquers, and glazes to every imaginable mass produced article which requires a finish for decorative or protective purposes.

A spray gun is a precision tool which relies on compressed air for its energy or power. Paint and compressed air are directed separately into the spray gun and by a system of air channels and a paint passageway the air is aimed at the paint stream at the head of the gun. This stream of compressed air imparts additional motion to the material being applied, and since every material has a critical speed at which it will break up or *atomize*, the material is therefore broken up into small spheres or globules—this action being known as *atomization*.

The force of the compressed air performs two functions. First it atomizes the paint and second it vaporizes the solvents in the paint. By correct adjustment of air pressure and the amount of fluid fed to the gun, it is possible to accurately control the degree of atomization, thus ensuring maximum atomization with the least vaporization of the solvents.

Operation The mechanical action of the spray gun may be described as follows. Fluid enters the spray gun through the fluid inlet immediately below the spray head of the gun, and is forced past a needle valve (the *fluid needle*) and out through the *fluid tip* or nozzle in the form of a jet or stream. The pressure driving the fluid may be created by gravity (by mounting the fluid container on top of the gun), by suction from the flow of air through the gun, or by use of a pump or a pressurized fluid container. A spring loaded valve, operated by the gun trigger, controls the supply. From the compressed air supply, air enters the gun through the air inlet at the bottom of the spray gun handle. It passes through the gun body and is projected through a series of small holes in a *baffle ring* behind the *air cap* which surrounds the fluid nozzle. The air supply is regulated by another spring loaded valve, also under trigger control.

Above: a paint spray gun driven by a small electrically powered air compressor. The paint is carried in the container below the gun.

Left: a cutaway diagram of a spray gun. The compressed air supply enters the gun through the air inlet at the bottom of the spray gun handle and passes through the lower spring loaded valve, which is controlled by the trigger of the gun. It then travels through the body of the gun to the fluid nozzle where it meets the paint flow which is leaving the gun under the control of the needle valve, which is also operated by the trigger, and adjusted by the upper spring loaded valve. The air and paint flows leave the nozzle in the air cap as a conical spray, and the cone can be flattened and widened into a horizontal, fan-shaped pattern by allowing air from the air cap's horns to impinge upon it. This air is controlled by the rear adjustment valve.

adjustment valve

spring loaded valve

baffle ring

spring loaded valve

nozzle

air cap horn

fluid inlet

spray gun handle

air inlet

When the trigger is depressed both valves act simultaneously, bringing the flows of fluid and air together, and the air directs the fluid stream into a conical spray pattern. This spray pattern can be altered to suit the work in hand by means of a spreader width adjustment valve mounted at the rear of the gun body. This valve alters the setting of an opening inside the gun, which regulates the flow of air through a second series of holes in the baffle ring to air ports contained in the two 'horns' of the air cap. These horns direct jets of air into the spray pattern from above and below.

The emission of air from these 'horn holes' impinges upon the conical spray, spreading it into an elongated shape, and by this means a horizontal fan shaped pattern can be achieved.

Types of gun Spray guns are made in various sizes and are classified according to their capacity to atomize and apply amounts of paint. They are rated for high, medium and low production requirements. The three principal parts of a spray gun are the air cap, the fluid tip, and the fluid needle. These are the parts which may be changed in a gun to make it more suitable for spraying one kind of material or another. The type of cap, tip or needle used depends on the type of paint to be sprayed and on the method of supplying paint to the gun (by suction, gravity or by pressure feed).

The amount or volume of air used by a spray gun is determined by the size and design of the air cap, and this is measured in terms of cubic feet (or cubic metres) per minute. Two types of air caps are generally available. One is the suction feed cap. This type is designed so that the air passing through the centre hole of the cap creates a vacuum in front of the fluid tip, thus allowing atmospheric pressure to force paint up to the spray gun from the container beneath it. The pressure feed cap is not basically designed to create a vacuum in front of the tip, and these caps are used in fast production where the fluid is fed to the spray gun by a pump or from a pressurized container.

The fluid tip is the part of the spray gun which meters the amount of paint flowing from the gun, and acts as a valve seat for the fluid needle. Fluid tips and needles are made in various sizes according to the viscosity and type of paint to be used.

The fluid needle is normally held in the closed position against the fluid tip by means of a spring, until withdrawn by the trigger action. The distance the needle is withdrawn, and thus the amount of fluid delivered, is controlled by the fluid adjusting screw.

Spray painting is a mechanical means of applying paint. The benefits derived by spray painting are economical application of finishing materials and high quality finishes at high rate of production. To enjoy these benefits it is important that the spray gun be regarded as a precision instrument and must be properly maintained and skilfully used in order to obtain maximum efficiency.

Electrostatic painting Many industrial painting processes, such as the application of primer paint to car bodies, now use ELECTROSTATIC painting systems. The object to be painted is given a negative electrostatic charge and passed through a mist of positively charged paint sprayed into the painting chamber. Electrostatic forces between the object and the paint attract an even layer of paint on to the surface of the object, including crevices that would not normally be reached. Finishing coats may subsequently be applied by conventional painting methods.

SPRING BALANCE (see weighing machines)

SPRINGS

Springs are mechanical devices which can store energy, using the elastic properties of the material of which they are made. ELASTICITY is that mechanical property which enables a material to be deformed linearly in proportion to an applied load, and to recover its shape with the removal of the load. The upper boundary of the elasticity is reached when the load results in permanent deformation; the maximum load which a material can sustain without permanent deformation is called the *elastic limit* or the *elastic modulus*.

Fluids Fluids, that is, gases and liquids, have no shape of their own but adopt the shape of their container. Liquids are virtually incompressible, but gases will adopt not only the shape but the size of their container, by expansion or compression, and are useful materials for absorbing shock or storing energy. *Shock absorbers* used in the SUSPENSION systems of motor vehicles are usually only damping devices for the coil springs in the system, but some designs, such as the German De Carbon system, actually compress the air in a piston and cylinder mechanism. Pneumatic shock absorbers are also used on machinery, such as the power presses used in SHEET METAL FORMING. A device using a compressible gas in an elastic container is the ordinary pneumatic TYRE, which absorbs some road shock in motor vehicles, but on aircraft has to absorb the tremendous shock of landing at high speeds.

Solids The variety of elastic properties among materials

Below: spring steel is drawn into the machine by rollers from a reel and pushed past formers to make a spring. Several hundred springs a minute can be formed and cut off this way. In the photo the spring wire can be seen pushed around the formers.

can be illustrated by comparing rubber and lead. A slug of rubber will, under pressure, expand to fill a limited space, and will recover its original shape when the load is removed. A slug of lead, on the other hand, will spread out under pressure to occupy a limited space, but remains in its deformed state when the load is removed. It can absorb energy but cannot store it; in other words, it has no elasticity and is of no use as a spring material.

Between these two extremes are metals such as copper, phosphor bronze and steel, which are each elastic to a certain limit. These are used as springs by varying elastically the geometry of the design of the spring. Metallic springs may be in the form of beams, washers, spirals, clips and so on; the design as well as the elasticity of the material must be capable of absorbing stress without permanent deformation.

Spiral springs Spiral springs are the most common type. They are flat or cylindrical (*helical*) in shape, or some variation of these, such as *conical* (tapering cylindrical) or *volute* (non-flat spiral). The force required to produce one unit of deflection is called the *stiffness*. The *spring rate* (or *spring constant*) is the load per unit of deflection and is inversely proportional to the number of active or working coils in the spring. The spring rate is *constant* if the coils are of equal pitch, and *variable* for unequal pitch; a variable load rate is also obtained from a conical spring. The spring rate will vary for a spring of a given size according to the material of which it is made.

A *close-coiled* helical spring has the coils wound so tightly that they are in contact with each other in the unloaded state of the spring; this type of spring is used as an *extension* spring, which means that it stores energy when it is stretched out. A spring used to close a door would be a good example. More

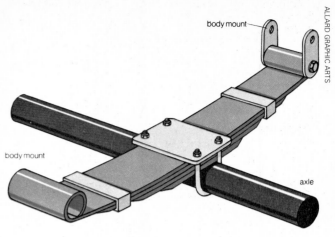

body mount

body mount

axle

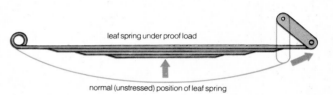

leaf spring under proof load

normal (unstressed) position of leaf spring

familiar is the *open-coiled* spring, used as a *compression* spring. An example would be the spring in a car seat or in a mattress.

Flat spiral springs are used in clockwork mechanisms and similar devices. They consist of a uniform thin strip wound on edge into a spiral on a flat plane; the outer end of the spiral is fixed to the mechanism and the inner end is shaped to receive the end of a shaft (key) by means of which it is wound up. Applying a torque to the shaft causes the coils to tighten into a smaller diameter, storing energy.

Leaf springs

Leaf springs are often used in cars, railway coaches and other vehicles. They are made up of a number of strips of spring-quality steel of varying lengths stacked together so that the shortest length (leaf) is nearest the source of the load. Leaf springs are supported at the ends and carry a central load (*semi-elliptic* or *simply supported*) or are supported at one end and carry a load at the other (*quarter-elliptic* or *cantilever* type). The strips are free to slide over one another

Left: the leaf spring, used in the last century on railway and horse-drawn carriages, is still used in the rear suspension of many cars. It has the advantage of locating the axle, allowing it to move up and down but not sideways, and also provides a small amount of damping as the steel strips slip against each other.

Below left: this little machine makes small springs of the type pictured on page 2212. A small closed coil is formed with straight ends, using pneumatic cylinders automatically closing formers.

Below: conical spiral springs such as those for upholstered seats being produced. As the spring is formed the forming mandrel moves away to allow a progressively wider spiral.

in service, and act as a laminated beam. Each leaf is given an initial curvature, and the load required to straighten a leaf spring is called the *proof load*. It is also called the *maximum design* load, because it causes the spring to 'bottom', or reach its maximum permissible deformation in service.

Manufacture

Coil springs are wound around a *mandrel* or *former*. For making small numbers of special-purpose springs, a LATHE may be used. The mandrel is inserted in the chuck, one jaw of the chuck is loosened, the bent end of the spring wire is inserted and the jaw tightened again. The lead screw of the lathe is engaged according to the number of coils per inch of the finished spring, and the tool post of the lathe is used to guide the wire on to the mandrel.

For mass production of springs, special-purpose machinery has been developed in which the spring wire is pulled off a reel by means of rollers and fed into the machine. It passes over a stationary mandrel and strikes a deflector plate, which makes it curl itself around the mandrel. At a pre-determined point in the machine cycle, the wire feed stops to allow the end of the spring to be cut off. Attachments can form the ends of the wire into hook shapes, or bend them or grind them so they are square (at a 90° angle to the length of the spring).

Springs can be machine produced at a rate of several hundred a minute. Spring wire of up to about 16 mm diameter is coiled cold, but above that size the coiling is usually undertaken at temperatures equivalent to hot FORGING or strip ROLLING operations.

Design

The choice of spring material and geometry depends upon working space, working temperatures, corrosion resistance, load frequency and required spring life, as well as the size of the load.

The designer uses mathematical formulae in making his decisions. For example, the energy stored in a flat spiral spring of length L to which a torque M has been applied, can be calculated from the expression $\frac{0 \cdot 5 (M^2) L}{EI}$ where E is the modulus of elasticity of the spring material and I is the *moment of* INERTIA of the material cross-section.

For most springs, ordinary carbon steels of the hard-drawn and oil-hardening type are satisfactory. Proper HEAT TREATMENT and tempering are necessary to remove internal stresses after cold-working in the coiling operation. For high temperature and high stress requirements, high-nickel alloy steel may be used; a stainless steel or non-ferrous alloy is used if corrosion resistance is necessary. Copper-base alloys are expensive, but are used for their electrical properties and corrosion resistance in electrical components and at sub-zero temperatures. Phosphor bronze is often used for contact fingers in switches on account of its low arcing properties. Some special nickel-base spring alloys have been developed to have a constant modulus of elasticity over a wide temperature range, and can be used in precision instruments where accuracy will be maintained despite fluctuation of temperature.

The most common cause of spring failure is *fatigue* over a number of cyclic stress variations of loading. Service life is numbered in terms of working cycles; for example, a spring which will not fail in more than 10,000,000 cycles is said to have an 'infinite' life, while failure below 100,000 cycles denotes 'short' life.

Below: the variety in size, shape and stiffness of available types of springs is enormous. Springs of one sort or another, often made of special alloys, are used in nearly all machines.

STABILIZER, ship

Stabilizers are designed to reduce the rolling of a ship in order to prevent cargo from shifting and causing a list. They also reduce problems for the catering services and increase passenger comfort on ferries and liners. For accurate gunfire on a warship a steady motion is necessary, and stabilizers are fitted to many naval vessels to control the angle of roll. Various types of stabilizer have been tried with varying degrees of success; these include *bilge keels*, *oscillating weights*, *anti-rolling tanks*, *gyroscopes* and *stabilizer fins*.

Bilge keels
These are normally fitted to the hull along both sides of the ship, and they extend for about one third of the length of the vessel. They are riveted or welded to the shell where it curves to form the bilge at the bottom of the ship. Bilge keels are attached so that they offer minimum resistance to the forward motion, and they are not too strongly connected to the hull so that they will break off without damaging the shell if they strike an obstruction. They present resistance to motion in the rolling direction by impeding the fluid flow around the hull, and they are more effective when the ship is under way than when it is stationary. Bilge keels are fairly effective at damping out the angle of roll and they tend to increase the period of roll, that is the time taken to roll from one side to the other and back again.

Below: a stabilizer fin mounted on a ship's hull. The motion of the fin through the water generates upward or downward forces, according to the angle of attack, to counteract the rolling motion of the ship. The angle of the fin is altered automatically by a hydraulic motor controlled by a gyroscope which senses the ship's motion.

Bottom: the stabilizer fin in its retracted position.

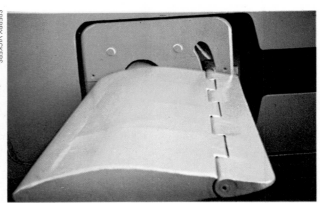

OSBORNE/MARKS

Three different arrangements for
stabilizing the rolling motion of ships.
The bottom diagram shows the ideal action
of a Frahm tank stabilizer; water moves
from one side of the tank to the other to
compensate for the wave motion. Centre left,
a stabilizer fin mounted in a ship's hull.
The fin can be rotated into the hull when
not in use, and the pitch can be varied
by a hydraulic vane motor whose action
is shown below right. On the right is an
activated tank stabilizer. The principle
of operation is the same as for a Frahm
stabilizer, but the water distribution
between the two sides of the tank is
determined by gyroscopically controlled
air valves.

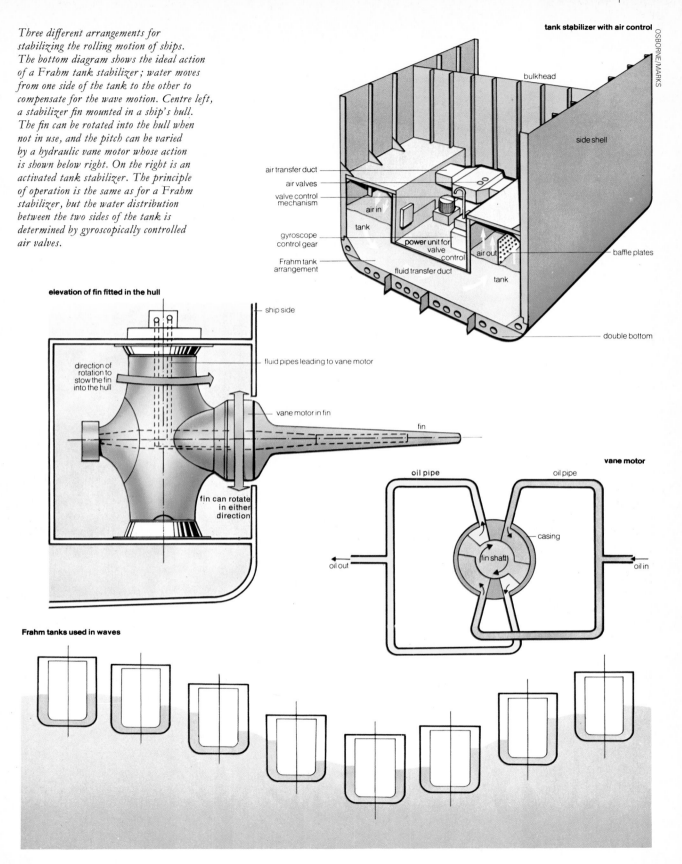

tank stabilizer with air control

bulkhead

side shell

air transfer duct
air valves
valve control mechanism
air in
tank
gyroscope control gear
power unit for valve control
air out
Frahm tank arrangement
fluid transfer duct
tank
baffle plates
double bottom

elevation of fin fitted in the hull

ship side
fluid pipes leading to vane motor
direction of rotation to stow the fin into the hull
vane motor in fin
fin
fin can rotate in either direction

vane motor

oil pipe
oil pipe
casing
fin shaft
oil out
oil in

Frahm tanks used in waves

Oscillating weights This system, now out of favour, involves moving weights from one side of a vessel to the other to counteract the motion created by the sea. The *phase* of the weight movement must lag 90 degrees behind the rolling motion of the vessel (the two movements must always be out of step) and thus the timing of the operation is critical. One method tried in an experimental installation was to move a truck on curved rails so that its weight produced a stabilizing force on the ship. Systems of this sort are no longer used partly because control in irregular waves is difficult and partly because they are noisy.

Anti-rolling tanks These were introduced very shortly after the first use of bilge keels. 'Frahm' anti-rolling tanks have been successfully used for a number of years on many ships. They are usually fitted near to amidships either in a tween deck space or lower down in the vessel above the double bottom. The arrangement is like a U-tube but with a larger cross-sectional area in the two vertical legs than in the horizontal leg. The relationship between these areas is important because the period of fluid oscillation when the ship rolls must be similar, but 90 degrees out of phase to that of the ship. There must be an air connection between the tops of the vertical tanks otherwise the air in one tank will become pressurized and the other tank will have a partial vacuum when the liquid levels change. An air valve in the connection gives a means of fluid control if necessary.

In *activated* anti-rolling tanks a high capacity, low pressure air compressor supplies air to the upper part of the tanks, and by varying the pressure in each tank water can be moved from one side of the ship to the other to give a stabilizing effect. A GYROSCOPE is used to stop and start the compressor and to operate the tank air valves as it senses the ship's motion.

Below: a stabilizer fin being fitted to a large Japanese ferry. The fin is made of steel castings and fabrications with an outer epoxy resin coating.

Gyroscopic stabilizers Some vessels are fitted with large gyroscopes to control rolling. This technique reduces the average angle of roll by about 50%. Schlick in Germany was the first to use this system, and later Sperry stabilizers were introduced in the United States. The Schlick gyroscope was installed with the spin axis vertical, and the support frame axis horizontal. When the vessel rolls the gyroscope frame swings in its bearings in a fore and aft direction. This is called *precession* and is a function of the gyroscopic action. A roll to starboard would cause the top of the gyroscope frame to move aft if unresisted at the bearings. The opposite will occur for a roll to port. Because the rolling of the ship causes precession of the gyroscope, if precessional motion is resisted by applying brakes to the bearings of the support frame this will set up a stabilizing effect in opposition to the rolling of the ship. Brake control of the Schlick type of stabilizer is difficult to achieve, and the Sperry stabilizers were arranged with a precession motor meshed with a vertical ring gear to precess the gyroscope in a direction to oppose the rolling motion of the ship. Control of the precession motor is by a small pilot gyroscope sensitive to the transverse motion of the ship. The pilot gyroscope operates electrical contacts which power the precession motor in the required direction.

Flume stabilization A *flume tank* is placed transversely across the ship and comprises two side compartments and a centre compartment, which contain water. The motion of the fluid from one side of the vessel to the other is controlled by a restriction called a *flume*. Liquid depth is constant in the centre compartment during the transfer process. The tanks are carefully designed to *tune* the liquid frequency to the natural period of roll of the vessel and to maintain the 90 degree phase relationship necessary for stabilization. The flume prevents the liquid movement from coming into phase with the ship's movement and causing a disastrous increase in the rolling.

Fins Stabilizer fins project from the hull and produce a turning moment on the ship to oppose any rolling motion. As

VOSPER THORNYCROFT LTD

the ship moves through the water, the flow over the protruding fins, port and starboard, is deflected according to the angle of the fin, producing either an upward or a downward stabilizing force. As the ship rolls, the fin on the ascending side of the vessel will generate a downward force and the fin on the other side will produce an upward force. The magnitude of these forces depends on the angle through which the fins are rotated from the horizontal position, and the speed of the water over the fin surface. At low ship speeds the fins are not so effective as when the vessel is travelling at her designed cruising speed. When not in use, the fins may be retracted into a watertight box in the hull, or they may be rotated forward into a watertight recess. An oil operated *vane motor* is used to turn the fins, the oil being delivered from a hydraulic pump controlled by a gyroscope which senses the ship's motion.

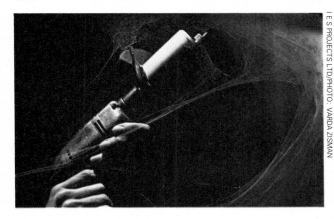

Above: a cobweb spinning machine. This consists of an electric drill with fan blades and cylinder containing a rubberized solution. The solution is extruded through fine slits and blown away by the fan.

STAGE EFFECTS

The term *stage effects* encompasses anything seen or heard during a theatrical performance not resulting directly from the action of a performer. The effects may be produced by mechanical manipulation of the scenery, by the use of sound, by the use of lighting, or by a combination of all three.

Scenic effects Increasing costs, and directors concentrating on the delivery of the text of a play, have meant that the full panoply of theatrical machinery is rarely used today, and only elementary scene-changes are made—usually by hand at the end of an act, though revolving stages are also used. In addition, melodrama, in which scenic effects were a main feature, was supplanted by the cinema, which also took over many of its devices for obtaining SPECIAL EFFECTS very early in its history.

Two traditional scenic effects are still used: *traps* and *gauze cloths*. Most modern traps consist of an ordinary trapdoor in the stage floor, through which the character or property rises on a lift. But in the nineteenth century elaborate *star traps* were popular, which could, for example, project a performer a few feet into the air for a spectacular entrance. As with many other stage effects, however, often the vital secret trick that made a special trap work was not divulged by the manufacturer.

There is no secret about a gauze cloth. When lit carefully only from the front it appears to be opaque, when lit from behind its transparency is revealed, and a rapid transformation of the scene achieved.

'Meteorological' effects Low-lying fog is produced

Below left: flying Valkyries in Wagner's opera created by lighting the figures behind a gauze cloth. With no rear lighting the cloth appears opaque but with rear lighting the 'flying' figures can be seen. The figures are drawn across by a cable and weights.

Below: the effect, as seen by the audience, is extremely realistic and is used in many situations where fade in/fade out is required.

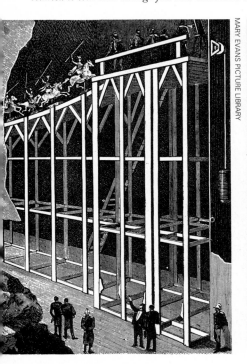

Above: an artificial smoke machine. The smoke, which is non-toxic and causes no deposits or damage to costumes, is produced by heating up a mineral oil. The oil is forced under pressure from a carbon-dioxide cylinder through a filter and jets into a heat exchanger.

Below: the ghost in this scene is produced by reflection off an angled glass sheet – the man below is brightly lit.

by releasing steam into a trough containing solid carbon dioxide (or 'dry ice'). Snow may be produced (somewhat unsatisfactorily) by a lighting effect, but the alternative method of releasing flakes of fireproof plastic from a slotted bag suspended in the *flies* (above the stage) is preferred by most directors. (Originally torn paper was used but this is now considered to be a fire hazard.) Similarly, projected rain effects are available, but they are not wholly satisfactory either. Rain, however, may be produced by releasing particles of fireproof plastic from the flies. Smoke is produced by a *smoke gun* containing an oil-based liquid which is heated by an element and the smoke propelled by carbon dioxide gas.

Lighting effects   Unusual lighting effects may be produced by purpose built devices, or, alternatively, normal equipment may be used. For example, to create the effect of a fire, neon flicker lamps together with a smoke effect and strips of silk blown by a fan can be used.

In some productions, scenery may be projected on to a suitable screen by front projection, or (if the depth of the stage allows) back projection. But the fact that large slides must be projected for long periods, from PROJECTORS using a very intense light at an always exact range and angle, makes this a difficult task to accomplish without considerable trouble and expense.

Moving film can be incorporated similarly. A mixture of stills, film, melting oil-slides, and flashing lights was developed as a means of obtaining 'psychedelic' effects in the late 1960s (see LIGHT SHOWS).

SONIA HALLIDAY

STAINED GLASS

All coloured glass is, in fact, 'stained' by the inclusion of appropriate metal oxides or other chemical compounds in the glass manufacture. The term, however, has come to refer to an art form, the creation of stained glass windows. Throughout the mediaeval period the art was known simply as *glazing* (the making of windows) or, in France and Germany, *vitrail* and *Glasmalerei* respectively.

Colours in glasses are produced by the absorption of certain wavelengths of incident light (see FILTER, optical) by IONS in solution in the glass (chromium ions produce green colours, cobalt ions blue and manganese ions purple), or by sub-microscopic particles precipitated from the glass melt at certain critical temperatures (copper or cadmium selenide are used for ruby). Larger particles, either having colour themselves, such as the excessive amount of chromium or copper compounds in *aventurine* glasses, or colourless as in opals, also produce colour.

A more specific use of the term 'stain' refers to a technique used by the artist to enhance the design. Silver oxide is applied usually to white glass which, after firing, results in a yellow stain.

History The earliest existing complete windows are those in the *clerestory* (see CATHEDRAL BUILDING) of Augsburg Cathedral, Germany (c 1065) and which are attributed to the monks of Tegernee. The technical completeness of these windows suggests that the art had originated much earlier and, being Italo-Byzantine in style, had evolved from the Hellenistic tradition. Another early example in Le Mans cathedral, France, shows similar Byzantine influence, but may have come to France independently by way of the Mediterranean Sea route to Spain. In England the earliest known glass (12th century) is reputedly in York Minster and is part of a panel depicting a seated king from a Jesse Tree window,

Above: 12th century rose window in the north-east transept of Canterbury Cathedral, England. The centrepiece may have been inserted under the direction of William of Sens, the architect.

Below: part of the original design and a section of its full-size cut line—a diagram from which the glass will be cut—whose lines are drawn to the thickness of the width of the leads' hearts.

LAWRENCE LEE

SONIA HALLIDAY

which is similar to panels in St Denis and Chartres, both in France. Some of the best examples of complete ranges of windows in the Early Gothic style of the twelfth and thirteenth centuries are in the cathedrals at Chartres and Canterbury.

The fourteenth century is characterized by a growing humanism in design and in the treatment of figures. The discovery of silver stain (silver oxide) earlier in the century, combined with the greater use of white or whitish glass, led to the general lightening of windows. By the fifteenth century, however, stained glass began to go into an artistic decline which persisted throughout the next two centuries.

The ability of glass painters to convey naturalistic effects was increased, in the seventeenth century, by the use of *enamels* (see ENAMELLING) which produced translucent colours when fired, avoiding the need to use separate areas of coloured glass. The window in New College Chapel, Oxford, painted to the *cartoons* (preliminary designs) of Sir Joshua Reynolds are typical.

In the nineteenth century the revival of interest in the art of the Middle Ages, in particular by the pre-Raphaelites, created windows which brought back some of the clarity of colour and design of early glass. This led to the many fine interpretations in modern twentieth century stained glass to be seen in the designs of Léger at Audincourt, France, and Matisse at Vence, France, and the windows at Coventry Cathedral, England. Technically, the rediscovery of making hand blown or '*muff*' glass, in the latter half of the nineteenth century contributed to this revival by making available a far better quality of glass. This type is called 'antique' glass.

Design, cutting A stained glass window is composed of variously shaped and coloured pieces of glass, with painted

Above: panel of a 15th century stained glass window by Hans Acker in Freiburg Cathedral, Germany, depicting the Last Judgement, which shows the beginning of the tendency towards naturalism in design.

Top right: a leading diagram is painted with black paint on the plate glass screen to indicate the positions of the leads so that the cut glass will be put into its appropriate position.

detail in line and shading, which are assembled in leads to form glazed panels.

Unlike the so-called 'fine art' painter, the stained glass artist has to consider his design strictly in relation to a given site, with precise measurements and structure, so that his completed work fits the window shape and stands up to adverse weather conditions. The original design is usually made to scale as in architectural drawing and includes the arrangement of the leading and the supporting bars. From this design a full-sized *cartoon* is made, either enlarging by hand on sheets of paper or by the use of photographic enlargement from the original.

When the cartoon is correct in all its details a *cut line* has to be made by means of laying detail paper over the cartoon and tracing through the leading pattern: this is the diagram from which the glass will be cut and its lines are thickened by pencil or ink to the width of the *heart* of the leads. The shapes of the glass are determined by the necessity to break down the images into the chosen colours (it being normally impossible to merge from one colour to another) and the restriction on the size which can be fixed safely. (It is, however, possible to change colours by *staining, enamelling* and *aciding*—see below.)

The cut line is laid over a plate glass table illuminated

LAWRENCE LEE

from underneath (called a *light box*), which enables the black lines of the cut line to show through all but the darkest of glasses. The selected glass is arranged over the diagram in the most economical way and cut to the *inside* edge of the thick line, while the contingent piece is cut to the other side of the line: this allows a narrow gap to be taken up by the heart of the lead. Cutting is nowadays done by means of a hardened steel *glass cutter* which is drawn firmly over the glass, and makes a scored line of sufficient depth to initiate a fracture with reasonable accuracy. After making this cut, the glass is fractured either by sharply bending the two sides at opposing angles if straight, or by tapping the underside of the cut with the back of the glass cutter if curved. The fractured glass is usually left with a ragged edge which is ground down with a *grozing iron*, a specially made pair of pliers having parallel jaws. When all the glass is cut and laid out on the cut line, it should fit the outside shape exactly leaving the spaces for the lead hearts.

Painting Techniques for painting the glass differ from one studio to another but, essentially, *iron oxides* are ground into a smooth paste with water and *gum arabic*, suitably diluted and applied to the glass with special long haired brushes called *tracers* which can make broad or fine lines. These traced lines are usually fired into the glass before the application of shading —called *matting*—which is effected by laying a thin wash of paint on the shadowed parts and graduating the tones by softening with a badger hair brush, pushing the paint from light to dark and sometimes stippling to give texture.

To fuse the paint or enamels to the glass it is then *fired* in a kiln. The pieces of glass are laid on a bed of plaster in metal trays warmed in a pre-heating chamber and placed in the firing chamber or '*muffle*'. As soon as glass has reached the correct temperature, about 620°C (1148°F), the painted surface will show an egg shell gloss and must be removed and placed in

Below : the pieces of selected coloured glass are being cut to the size appropriate for each section of the cut line. The glass cutter has a hard steel wheel and makes score lines on the glass which will fracture when tapped.

LAWRENCE LEE

Left: glass is laid over the cartoon and the main lines of the composition traced on with tracing brushes. The wrist is positioned on a wooden rest to ensure accuracy.

Below left: completed panel before fixing. On the bench can be seen the battens and glazing nails—horseshoe nails are generally preferred to carpenter's nails.

Right: detail of the Last Judgement, St Mary's Church, Fairford, Gloucestershire, 16th century. Last Judgement windows are often referred to as 'Doom' windows. This window is full of Flemish detail, owing to the influence of the technical advances in painting mainly by Flemish glass painters. The Virgin kneels on the left of Christ (seated on a rainbow); on the right, John the Baptist wearing his camel hair robe. Around the centrepiece are angels, apostles and martyrs.

Far right: Fortitude, Charity and Hope, painted by Thomas Jervais, 1778, designed by Sir Joshua Reynolds, New College, Oxford, England.

the warmest of the cooling racks beneath the firing chamber. It is then brought down progressively until, at the lowest rack, it is cool enough to remove. This process is repeated until all the trays are fired. The glass may be fired a second time if the lines or *matts* need strengthening. When silver stain (silver oxide) is to be used for additional colouring, a further firing is necessary, but this time at a lower temperature—about 520 to 550°C (968 to 1022°F).

Areas of colour may be produced also by *aciding*. Some coloured glasses are made by *casing* or *flashing* the basic white glass with a coloured film (usually red or blue because these colours tend to be very dark if used throughout a glass) by dipping the molten glass 'bubble' in a crucible of the required colour and blowing again until the coating of colour is thinned out over the whole surface. This 'flashed' glass allows the artist to remove areas of the coloured film by etching it away with hydrofluoric acid, after masking out the parts to be retained as colour. This makes complicated details, for example in heraldic work, much easier to design. Before the nineteenth century the only means of removing the 'flash' was by grinding through the film with a glass engraving wheel.

Leading During the cutting and painting operations, the glass is usually stuck up for checking on large glass screens placed in their proper position with the aid of a diagram of the leading drawn on the back of the screen. On completion of painting and firing the glass is taken down and laid out

ready for glazing. The leads or *calmes* are fabricated from a lead strip passed through a lead mill which forms them into the characteristic H section; they are milled in several sizes from 0.12 inch (0.32 cm)—called string leads—to wide border leads 0.6 inch (1.6 cm) wide. Leading up begins by placing border leads against battens fixed to the glazing bench at right angles. The glass is introduced progressively from the corner formed by the right angle until the panel is completed. Each piece of glass is surrounded by a lead cut to the appropriate size so that junctions of leads for the various shapes butt into each other to form a neat joint. The size of the glazed panel depends on the dimension of the window and the best size for handling during fixing.

When the leading is completed on the panel, each joint is rubbed with *tallow* to act as a flux and soldered. The panel is then turned over and the procedure is repeated. The panels must then be made weathertight and this is done by *cementing* with a compound made of equal parts of plaster of Paris and whiting, mixed with equal parts of boiled oil and turpentine; lamp black and a little red lead is also added. The cement is therefore a liquid form of putty. It is rubbed into the leads on both sides with scrubbing brushes and then dried off by sprinkling plaster of Paris over the panel and scrubbing until all the unwanted cement is removed from the glass. After leaving to harden, the cement joins are cleaned back and again left to harden for several days before fixing. Each section is

SONIA HALLIDAY

SONIA HALLIDAY

then *banded*, that is, copper *ties* are soldered on to hold the glass firmly to the saddle bars.

Fixing   The installation of the window into the architectural frame is carried out by skilled lead glaziers. In a multipanel window the sections will have been made so that the top border lead of the first section (fixing always begins from the base) will fit into the border lead of the next panel. The panels are worked into the stone grooves of the window frames and the *saddle bars* are fixed at predesigned intervals (usually about one foot or 30 cm apart) so that the window is supported throughout its height. Saddle bars are mostly of iron (they may be tipped with bronze to prevent rusting in the stone work) and let into the stone by drilling holes deep enough to take the tip of each side. The copper ties, fixed to line up with the bars, are now passed around the bar and twisted off.

Finally, the window is *pointed up*, inside and out, with mortar to fill the grooves and obtain a smooth joint against the border leads of the glass. If the stained glass is fixed into metal or wooden frames, putty glazing is used. The panels are placed into the rebate, and after puttying the retaining beads are screwed back.

Technical developments   The art of glazing has remained virtually unaltered until comparatively recently. *Slab* glass, or *dalles de verre* as it is called in France, is a development of moulded glass producing one inch (2.54 cm) thick slabs of glass, in brilliant colours. Since these slabs cannot be

fired or fixed into leads, a form of mosaic design has developed which uses glass shapes and black bonding cement: cement in this case is the building mix of cement and sand in the usual proportions, with colouring agent, poured over the glass and worked into the spaces until the whole panel is cast. This form of cement has proved unreliable and has been replaced by *epoxy mortar*, a mixture of epoxy resin and 'fillers'.

Glass mosaic or *glass appliqué* is made possible by the availability of epoxy resin. Here the normal 'antique' glass is cut to the design and stuck down on plate glass with the clear resin. Since this adhesion has a chemical rather than a mechanical action the panel of glass must be kept flat and left to cure for at least a day before *grouting*, which is the rubbing in of a compound of fine sand and black colouring mixed with a *plasticizer*. This fills in little cracks of light between the pieces of glass and reinforces the drawing of the design.

Experiments with industrial products such as resins have led to the production of artifacts which may be free standing, in fact, glass sculptures. *Fused glass* is produced by the fusing together of coloured glasses at the melting temperature in prearranged shapes and bonded together as decoration panels or 'sculptures'. A kiln at a greater temperature than the usual glass firing kiln is necessary for this process.

STAINLESS STEEL (see alloy & steel)

STAMP PRINTING (see gravure process)

STAPLING

Stapling, developed originally in the 19th century for paper attachment in the office, has become a highly specialized industry. As well as being indispensable for everyday office paperwork, modern stapling serves a variety of industries, for example, furniture making and upholstering, shopfitting, display and exhibition work, carton and bag closing in the packaging field, and binding by securing papers at their centrefold.

Staples are U-shaped pieces of wire supplied in the form of a continuous channel or strip of metal which has transverse lines of weakness impressed along its length to define the individual staples. The strip is placed in the *raceway* or magazine of the stapler, and a blade in the machine breaks off the staples from the strip as it drives them into the materials to be joined.

In all types of stapling the principle is the same; pressure is applied to the *crown* or top of the staple by a blade within the machine. Staples are automatically fed into position beneath the blade from the spring loaded raceway, and the driving force is supplied by hand, spring, electricity or compressed air. With the everyday office stapler, including *stapler pliers* which work on the lever-fulcrum principle, the papers to be attached together are placed between the stapler head and an *anvil* with shaped grooves accurately aligned beneath it. The staple legs, set at right angles to the crown, pierce the papers and then, coming into contact with the anvil grooves, are bent flat. The anvil is usually adjustable to two positions offering two sets of grooves; one shaped to guide the staple legs inwards for permanent attachment, and the other to guide them outwards for pin-type temporary attachment.

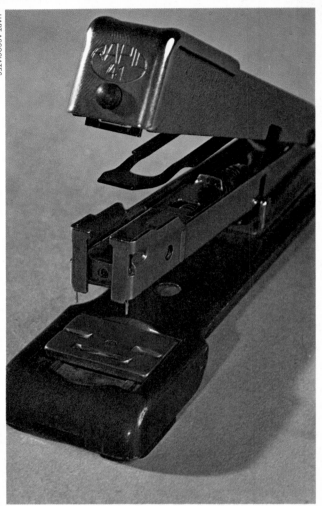

HART ASSOCIATES

OFREX LTD

Above: a typical office stapler. A strip of staples is positioned in the raceway, and the blade which breaks off the individual staples can be seen projecting from the front of the upper arm of the machine. A two-position anvil (lower front) allows the staple legs to be bent either inwards or outwards.

Left: a pneumatic tacker is used to fix together pieces of wood.

The number of papers which can be stapled together will depend on the thickness of the paper and the length and thickness of the staple legs. Increased capacity models are available for situations in which standard staplers are inadequate, and long-arm machines are used where greater reaching capacity is needed. The size of the staple, the gauge and composition of the metal wire, the ratio of leg length to crown width, and the angle of the legs' points all contribute, along with the anvil (or lack of it for some purposes) to the staple's subsequent efficiency.

Industrial staplers The development of models for high volume work on a greater variety of materials from hardboard and light metals to plastics and textiles owes much to the increased driving power of modern stapling machines, together with advances in the design and precision manufacture of the staple itself.

Industrial stapling machines are very often required to drive staples whose legs will pierce materials and drive through them, but remain unclinched afterwards. These are known as *tackers* and they do not require an anvil. In common use throughout the world for fastening upholstery and joining timber, these machines derive from the basic tacker used to attach papers to noticeboards. Trigger-operated industrial tackers are usually pneumatic, powered by compressed air. They offer accurate high speed working and can be used singly or in multiple installations controlled from a single point. They can also be incorporated into automatic production or assembly lines.

Related to staplers are pneumatic *hog ring machines* which have an anvil designed to bend the staple legs together with the crown into a tight ring around the twisted neck of a bag. They are used to secure filled sacks and bags made of paper, polyethylene and mesh without piercing the material.

STARTER

A starter is a machine for rotating the crankshaft of an engine from rest to a speed at which the engine will commence to operate on its own. The starters used for INTERNAL COMBUSTION ENGINES are usually battery operated, direct current ELECTRIC MOTORS, ranging in power from 0.5 hp on MOTORCYCLE engines up to 15 hp on very large DIESEL ENGINES.

The motors used are *series wound* and *short time rated*, that is, the windings of the rotor and stator are electrically connected in series, and the motor is designed to produce a high power output for a short period of time without exceeding a specified temperature. The series winding characteristics give the starter the large initial *torque* (turning force) it requires to overcome the static INERTIA and FRICTION of the engine, and to accelerate it up to speed in the shortest possible time to avoid too heavy a drain on the battery.

The starter is a dead weight while the engine is running, and so it must be as light and small as possible. To achieve this the starters are short time rated at two or three minutes: if

a starter motor was required to deliver its maximum power over longer periods of time it would have to be bigger and heavier to avoid overheating.

The starter requires a heavy current to operate it. This is of the order of 150 amps on a medium sized CAR and 1000 amps on the very big COMMERCIAL VEHICLES. The switching of this current is accomplished by means of a RELAY or SOLENOID operating a set of electrical contacts. The relay or solenoid in its turn is operated by a switch which is usually controlled by a key, and is placed in the driving cab of the vehicle.

Engagement with the engine is made through a pair of GEARS, the ratio of which is about 12 to 1, the larger gear being that on the engine. The smaller gear, known as the *pinion*, is positioned on the shaft of the starter, and the larger one is mounted on the housing of the CLUTCH of the engine and is known as the *ring gear*. There are two methods by which this gear is engaged, the *inertia method* and the *pre-engaged method*.

Inertia starters   The inertia starter uses the rapid acceleration of the starter armature, acting on the inertia of the pinion, to create a force which will drive the pinion up a helix on the shaft of the starter and hence into mesh with the ring gear. When the engine is running and the starter is switched off, the pinion is driven back down the helix and out of mesh with the ring gear.

A heavy spring known as a *buffer spring* is positioned on the shaft to absorb the force of the pinion as it is flung out of mesh, and a light spring is used to hold the pinion out of mesh while the engine is running. This type of starter is used on small and medium sized cars.

Pre-engaged starters   The pre-engaged starter is widely used on both petrol [gasoline] and diesel engines. The relay which operates the starter is replaced by a solenoid mounted on the starter, which is used to move the pinion up to and into mesh with the ring gear before switching on the

Below: an inertia starter. When the motor is switched on the pinion is driven along the helix on the shaft so that it engages with the ring gear on the engine.

current to the starter motor. In order to ensure entry when the teeth of the pinion and the teeth of the ring gear are not perfectly in line, some means of *indexing* the pinion gear (rotating it so that it is correctly aligned with the ring gear) must be provided. One such method is to arrange for the solenoid to compress a spring before it switches on the motor, so that on switching on, the pinion is rotated and the spring forces it into mesh.

The starter can now be held in mesh even after the engine is running, and to prevent damage to the starter an overrunning device is fitted to the pinion. A roller clutch, which is a form of *freewheel*, is one such device. This consists of an outer race and an inner race, one of which is circular, the other having a series of taper steps so adjusted as to give a series of reductions in the gap between the two races. There is a springloaded roller bearing in each of these taper steps, the springs forcing the rollers into the reduced gaps. Rotating the drive in one direction will jam the rollers into the gaps and lock the two races together, so that torque is transmitted. Rotation in the other direction will cause the rollers to free, allowing the races to freewheel.

The pre-engaged system is a necessity for diesel engines which are inherently more difficult to start than petrol [gasoline] engines because of the high compression ratios used. In spite of being more expensive than the inertia system, the preengaged system is becoming more popular for a wider range of applications, since it is quieter and will operate better over a wider temperature range.

Below: a pre-engaged starter, which uses a solenoid to drive the pinion into mesh before current is supplied to the motor. The solenoid is inside the cylindrical housing on top of the motor.

STATICS and hydrostatics

Statics is a branch of science which considers the forces acting on an object when it is at rest relative to its surroundings. It is one of the two major aspects of mechanics, the other being DYNAMICS, which considers moving objects.

Statics is really a particular case of dynamics and the laws relating to the action of forces on moving objects are valid for the particular case of bodies at rest. Historically however, statics developed as a science long before dynamics on the basis of laws independent of the idea of motion. The earliest systematic studies to lay the foundation of statics was made by ARCHIMEDES of Syracuse (287 to 212 BC). The principles of statics can be extended to the study of fluids and of objects immersed in fluids, and this is termed *hydrostatics*.

Principles of statics   A *force* may be considered as a physical influence, a push or a pull, which when applied to an object tends to cause motion. The effect produced depends on the force magnitude and on the direction in which it is applied. Force is thus termed a *vector* quantity, in contrast to quantities having only magnitude, which are termed *scalar* quantities.

When vectors such as forces act along the same line the combined effect can be found by adding their magnitudes when acting in the same direction or by subtracting them when oppositely directed. The combined effect of a number of applied forces is termed the *resultant* of the system. The resultant of forces acting in different, non-parallel directions may be found by application of the *parallelogram law*, which states that if two forces acting at a point are represented by the adjacent sides of a parallelogram, then the resultant is represented by the diagonal of that parallelogram. For a large number of such forces the resultant may be found by repeatedly applying the parallelogram law to the forces, two at a time.

Above: statics is very important in the design of bridges and other structures. It enables the designer to calculate the maximum loads that the structure can withstand. Note the interconnecting triangular structures—the triangle is a very stable shape.

Left: vessels for deep sea diving must be capable of withstanding the enormous pressures—statics helps determine the design.

For a body to be in *equilibrium*, that is, stationary relative to its surroundings, the resultant of the forces acting must be zero. If there are two forces acting, then they must exactly oppose each other in direction and be of equal magnitude. Three non-parallel forces acting on a body to produce an equilibrium situation must have lines of action that all pass through a common point. Under such circumstances the vectors representing the three forces form a triangle in which the force directions follow each other around the sides of the triangle. This rule is widely applied in statics and is known as the *Triangle of Forces theorem*: the length and direction of each side of the triangle is proportional to the magnitude and direction, respectively, of each force.

This can be extended to situations where any number of non-parallel forces act at a point on an object. It is found that the vector representation of these forces results in a closed polygon (a many-sided figure) when the forces are in equilibrium. The force directions follow each other around this polygon as in the case of the previously described triangle.

When forces act at a point on an object they tend to produce movement of the point. When, however, forces act on a body without meeting at a point, there is a tendency for the body

CROWN COPYRIGHT

BASF

to rotate as well as moving along a straight line. The rotating effect of a force about any point is termed the *moment* of the force about that point, and is measured by multiplying the force magnitude by the perpendicular distance of its line of action from the point considered. For such a body to be in equilibrium, the sum of the moments of forces tending to cause rotation in one direction must be equal to the sum of the rotating influences in the opposite direction. This is known as the *principle of moments*.

Thus for equilibrium, the forces applied to a body must have a zero resultant and a net moment of zero about any point, and the application of these conditions to various practical situations forms the basis of statics.

In addition to any external applied forces, most practical problems in statics involve the force due to the Earth's gravitational attraction acting on the body and frictional forces at the points of contact between the body and contacting objects. The weights of the constituent particles comprising any body form a system of parallel forces which can be effectively replaced by a single force. For this to be an effective resultant of the system, it must act through some specific determinable point, which is known as the *centre of gravity* of the body. The position of this is of fundamental importance in determining the stability of an object when disturbed from an equilibrium situation.

If the line of action of the force of gravity acting through the centre of gravity remains within the base of the object when disturbed, it exerts a turning moment that tends to restore equilibrium. The body is then said to be *stable*. The equilibrium is described as *unstable* when the vertical through the centre of gravity falls outside the base of the object, as the moment exerted by the force of gravity then tends to topple the object. If the position of the centre of gravity relative to the base remains unchanged by a disturbance, the equilibrium is said to be *neutral*.

The frictional force between objects in contact is brought into play when the two objects tend to move relative to each other, this force providing a RESISTANCE to such motion (see also FRICTION).

An important branch of statics concerns the study of forces acting on structural frameworks (see FRAME CONSTRUCTION). These are normally triangular arrangements, since this is the only geometrical shape that cannot be altered without deformation of the components in the framework. If forces are assumed to be applied at the ends of the structural rods, they must act along the length of the rods in order to balance each other. If these forces tend to extend the rod, it is termed a *tie*,

Top left: balloons rise when the mass of air they displace is greater than the mass of the balloon itself—this is Archimedes' principle, an important principle in hydrostatics.
Left: testing a synthetic material under heavy loads to determine its mechanical properties. The internal stresses and strains produced by the application of an external load are determined by the material, shape and dimensions—a complex problem in statics.

Right: forces must be summed vectorally to find their resultant (simple case: when forces are parallel). A set of forces is in equilibrium when their resultant is zero—for example, any point on a supported beam or framework which is stationary (static). Equilibrium conditions (stable, unstable and neutral) are important in some statics problems. A fluid is static when the pressure is constant at a given height. Hydraulic systems can amplify forces.

ALLARD GRAPHIC ARTS

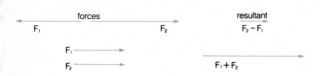

forces

F_1 F_2

resultant

$\overline{F_2 - F_1}$

F_1

F_2

$F_1 + F_2$

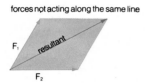

forces not acting along the same line

F_1 resultant

F_2

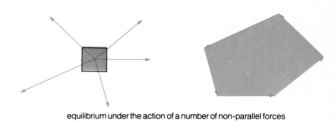

the resultant of a system of forces

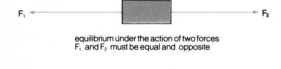

F_1 F_2

equilibrium under the action of two forces
F_1 and F_2 must be equal and opposite

equilibrium under the action of a number of non-parallel forces

F_1

F_2

F_3

F_1

F_3

F_2

equilibrium under the action of 3 forces

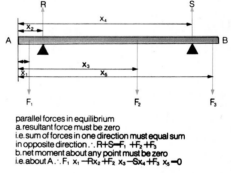

parallel forces in equilibrium
a. resultant force must be zero
i.e. sum of forces in one direction must equal sum
in opposite direction ∴ $R + S = F_1 + F_2 + F_3$
b. net moment about any point must be zero
i.e. about A ∴ $F_1 \, x_1 - Rx_2 + F_2 \, x_3 - Sx_4 + F_3 \, x_5 = 0$

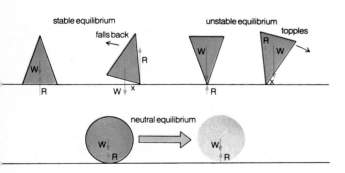

stable equilibrium

falls back

unstable equilibrium

topples

neutral equilibrium

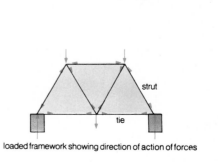

strut

tie

loaded framework showing direction of action of forces

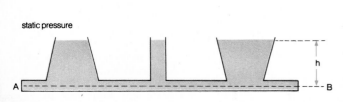

static pressure

A   h   B

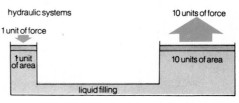

hydraulic systems

1 unit of force

10 units of force

1 unit
of area

10 units of area

liquid filling

and if the rod is in compression it is referred to as a *strut*.

The rules of statics provide the means of calculating, and so predicting, the forces acting in the structural members of any such construction. This information, allied to a consideration of the strength of available construction material, enables the planning and building of structures suitable for the intended application.

Hydrostatics

The theory of statics can be extended to deal with the equilibrium of *fluids* and of bodies immersed in fluids, where a fluid is considered as a material whose constituent particles act upon each other with forces *normal* (perpendicular) to their common surface.

Since hydrostatics concerns the study of fluids in equilibrium, the cohesive forces within the fluid which are responsible for fluid VISCOSITY can be ignored. The term fluid applies to liquids or gases, a liquid being defined as a fluid which is practically incompressible, whereas a gas is easily compressed and is capable of indefinite expansion to fill any space that contains it (see MATTER). The *density* of a fluid is the mass of a unit volume of that fluid. Since a fluid has weight, it exerts a thrust on any surface in contact with it. If the system is in equilibrium, the thrust is always exerted at right angles to the contact surface.

The thrust acting per unit area of contact surface is termed PRESSURE, and this increases with increasing depth in the fluid. The pressure exerted by a fluid also depends on its *density*. At any point in the fluid the pressure is equal to the depth multiplied by the density. The pressure exerted on the Earth's surface by its atmosphere at sea level is approximately the same as the pressure exerted by a column of water 10 metres (34 ft) high. The density of mercury is 13.6 times greater than that of water, and consequently an equivalent pressure is given by a much shorter column of mercury (760 mm, 30 in).

The pressure at any depth in a fluid acts equally in all directions and at right angles to the surface of any object immersed in the fluid. This pressure within a liquid plays an important part in many branches of engineering. The retaining walls of a dam need to be much thicker at the base than at the top in order to withstand the greater pressure, and SUBMARINE vessels must be engineered to be of sufficient strength to withstand the pressures exerted by the water at the depths at which they are designed to operate.

PASCAL'S Law is an extremely important law in hydrostatics: it states that pressure applied to a liquid in a closed, completely filled container is transmitted equally to all parts of the container in contact with the liquid. The pressure is exerted in a direction perpendicular to the walls of the container. This principle is the basis of operation of many types of HYDRAULIC devices such as presses, jacks and braking systems. The total exerted thrust may be scaled up by transmitting the applied force through a liquid filling the space between two pistons of different surface area.

Another important hydrostatic principle is that discovered by the Greek Archimedes. He discovered that an object submerged in a fluid is acted upon by an upward force equal to the weight of the fluid that the object displaces. The volume of fluid displaced by a submerged object is equal to the volume of that object. If the mass of that volume of fluid is greater than the mass of the object, that is if the object is less dense than the fluid in which it is placed, the upward force exerted by the fluid causes the object to float.

Below: application of hydrostatics at a drilling rig. Special chemicals are mixed with water (or other fluid) in the tank on the left and forced under pressure down the drill hole to cool the bit. The fluid returns to the surface carrying with it the cuttings.

ESSO